HACKING
THE COSMOS

HOW REVERSE ENGINEERING UNCOVERS
ORGANIZATION, INGENUITY AND THE CARE OF A MAKER

Dominic M. Halsmer, PhD PE

Kendall Hunt
publishing company

Cover image © Shutterstock.com

www.kendallhunt.com
Send all inquiries to:
4050 Westmark Drive
Dubuque, IA 52004-1840

Copyright: © 2019 by Dominic M. Halsmer

ISBN: 978-1-5249-8958-3

Published in the United States of America

COVERS EXPLANATION

Front and back covers present photographic images of colliding galaxies courtesy of the Hubble Space Telescope. According to NASA, these seemingly catastrophic occurrences, in which spiral appendages are often torn clean off, actually result in new star formation, with the accompanying creation of heavier chemical elements needed for life. For more details on these images, go to https://apod.nasa.gov/apod/ap150201.html (front cover) and https://apod.nasa.gov/apod/ap171019.html (back cover).

DEDICATION

for Petes' sake

CONTENTS

CONTENTS

PREFACE

Over the past twenty-seven years of teaching engineering at Oral Roberts University, I often found myself, along with my students, wrestling with issues in science and theology, but from an engineering point of view. I began to see how theology and the various sciences were not the only fields needed in this discussion. It became clear that the field of engineering should also have a seat at the table, since God appears to be involved in some kind of cosmic and spiritual engineering project. I was soon conducting research with students from several academic disciplines, exploring the applicability and implications of this perspective.

A few years and several publications later, I began to think that a book was needed to codify the findings. Since I understood part of my calling to be that of helping the typical Christian-in-the-pew better understand, and perhaps resolve, science and faith issues, it seemed best to write the book for a popular audience, geared toward young people, and requiring no specialized knowledge. This is what I have tried to do. Since these issues often tend to be intensely personal, I have also flavored each chapter with historical accounts from my own journey. But fear not, my dubious attempts at poetry have been relegated to the endnotes.

These personal stories should help to ease readers into some of the more technical material and see how it fits in the overall scheme. I also hope these stories will help people to develop the kind of familiarity, commonality, and trust that leads to increased unity among Christians in the midst of a diversity of views on these issues. Ultimately, I hope you will get to know God better through reading this book, which should enhance all your relationships, but especially the one with your Maker.

ACKNOWLEDGMENTS

It would be hypocritical to write such a book and not thank my Maker first and foremost, for all of the reasons discussed herein. Thank you God, for having the idea of me, making me so ingeniously, and then going to all the trouble to get me out of trouble. I would be nowhere without you.

My wife, Kate, deserves many thanks for loving and supporting me throughout this lengthy project, as do our four children, Nicholas, Christina, Mary Kate, and Josephine. My mother, Josephine, deserves credit for providing a great example to follow since she authored the book describing my dad's life just a few years earlier. Their unconditional love gave me direction and helped to guide me home, shining brightly like the North Star to an airplane pilot who has just lost all the instruments due to an unexpected electrical failure.

To some degree, the impetus for this project was provided by another author and former colleague, Jadell Forman, who was one of the first people to say that she enjoyed my writing. I'm grateful to her and several other colleagues who have helped me think through many of these issues: Leslie Wickman, Susan Slade, C. John Collins, Randy Isaac, John Korstad, Hal Reed, Calvin Roso, Andrew Lang, Ken Weed, Don Vance, Chris Green, Bill Collier, Bill Ranahan, Lanny Endicott, Paul Vickery, Myra Bloom, Dave Steensland, Stephen Frezza, Nate Meleen, and William Lyons. I'm also thankful to Jeff Dunn for his many excellent suggestions during the final edit. They were all accepted.

In addition, I'm grateful to all the Oral Roberts University students who have played such a big part in shaping this work (and me) over the years. Sincere thanks goes out to all the students who have served on my science and faith research team, especially Robbie Johnson, James Wanjiku, Nicholas Halsmer, Nate Roman, Tyler Todd, Michael Gewecke, Rachelle Gewecke, Jon Marc Asper, Elliot Butay, Ben Hase, Sean McDonough, Taylor Tryon, Joshua Weed, Kyle Hansen, Jessica Fitzgerald, Benjamin Zigrang, Joshua Beck, P. Wesley Odom, Jordan Mendenhall, Gabriel Kanelopoulos, Caleb Lutz, Joshua Williams, Emily Dzurilla, Daniel Rykert, Josie Halsmer, Alex Mills, John Voth, Oluwafishomi Philip King, DeWayne Bryant, Philip Riegert, David Meddaugh, Nathan Way, and Chloe Busse.

ABOUT THE AUTHOR

Dominic Michael Halsmer is a Professor of Engineering at Oral Roberts University in Tulsa, Oklahoma. His education includes Bachelor's and Master's Degrees in Aeronautical and Astronautical Engineering from Purdue University, a PhD in Mechanical Engineering from UCLA, and a Master of Arts Degree in Biblical Literature from ORU. He received the Scholar of the Year Award from ORU in 2000 and 2015, as well as outstanding teaching awards in 1997, 2001, 2003, 2005, 2014, 2017, and 2019. He served as a NASA Fellow at Goddard Space Flight Center in 1996 and 1997 through the ASEE Summer Faculty Fellowship Program. He served as Dean of the ORU College of Science and Engineering from 2007 to 2012. He also served as Director of the Center for Faith and Learning at ORU from 2013 to 2016.

His current research involves engineering education, reverse engineering, and contributions from the field of engineering to the science and faith conversation. He and his undergraduate student research team have produced many publications in all of these areas. He and his wife, Kate, have four children: Nicholas, Christina, Mary Kate, and Josie, and two grandchildren: Sydney and Zeke. Dominic and Kate reside in Jenks, Oklahoma, where he enjoys worshiping God through teaching, research, trail running, disc golf, ultimate Frisbee, sand volleyball, cross-fit, basketball, gardening, salsa-making, chess, and reading up on science and faith issues.

PART I
Science, Engineering, and Christian Faith

CHAPTER ONE

Defusing the Explosive Issue of Human Origins

FAST TIMES AT CENTRAL CONFLICT HIGH

"So then, where *did* you get the alcohol?" The unusually stern look on Principal Vernon's face caused his sharply spoken words to have a paralyzing effect, as if they had pinned me to the overstuffed chair in his office. I knew Mondays could be tough, but this particular Monday morning, during the fall semester of my sophomore year at Central Catholic High School, was turning out to be a real prizewinner. My memories of the previous Friday night's reckless activities were hazy at best. I remembered walking with two of my classmates to one of their houses after the homecoming football game, where we managed to find, and make off with, a large bottle of whiskey.

On our way back to the homecoming dance, we had stopped in a field and, sitting in a circle, passed the bottle around until we polished it off. I remember laughing so hard at the feeling of being drunk for the first time, and the excitement of sharing the experience with two of my good friends. I should have realized right then, when it became difficult to sit up, that maybe this wasn't such a good idea, and that getting up and stumbling back to the dance in the school cafeteria was an even worse idea. But then, I hadn't thought very far ahead that fateful evening. Even though I was getting straight As in school, and had a reputation for being savvy in basketball and football games, I was not very intelligent when it came to social situations.

I couldn't remember much after that, except finally waking up at home the next day with a pounding headache, a knotted and thoroughly empty stomach, and a horrible taste in my exceedingly dry mouth. Over the next several minutes, a few of my family members, of which there were many (I was number eleven of thirteen children), filled in some of the remaining ugly details. Evidently, I *had* successfully made it back to the dance, where I proceeded to puke my guts out in grand fashion. Someone then helped me make it to the restroom (bless their soul), where, eventually, my parents and older brothers discovered me, gloriously passed out on the tile beneath a toilet. But not before my inebriated condition was knowingly observed by a few of our teachers and school administrators. I was called into the school office that next Monday morning, where I confessed the whole story, or at least what I could remember, including (without any awareness of the obvious and far-reaching consequences—remember my social ineptitude?) the names of my two friends!

As you can imagine, they were immediately called in and questioned as well. The fact that I had just implicated my two friends hit me like a ton of bricks, and I was kicking myself for not realizing the obvious: that my decision to simply confess everything was sure to get them in big trouble too. But to my surprise, since they had not been observed in a drunken state at the dance, they had both quickly decided to deny any involvement in the entire escapade. This left me with a tough decision. Do I stand by my original story? Or do I change it in an effort to exonerate my two friends?

Although I had been raised to know the importance of always telling the truth, it seemed fruitless in this situation to stick to my story, and have three people in trouble instead of just one. Such was my level of reasoning as a teenager. Of course, I also felt some peer pressure to go in this direction, so I summarily recanted my original story, and said that I had acted on my own in getting so drunk and disorderly. Thus I found myself in my current predicament, pinned against the hot seat in Father Vernon's office, embroiled in conflict on multiple fronts (family, friends, and school officials), and clueless about how to respond to his question, or what to do next.

Asking the Right Questions

Conflict seems to be an inevitable part of the world. Life can very quickly get a little crazy at times. Lots of wild things happen, both amazingly good and extraordinarily bad. It's enough to make us wonder if anyone is actually "running this show." That's a good question. In fact, that's the right question. The answer to this question greatly influences how we live our lives, and who we become. The universe seems engineered specifically to make us curious about many things, especially such "big questions" as the existence of God, and life after death. People have different answers to these questions, and that often results in conflict. This is one of the reasons why education is so valuable. School should satisfy our thirst for knowledge of the world and what it's all about, in addition to giving us a skill that enables us to earn a living.

But many academic institutions today focus solely on making students employable, without much regard for life's bigger questions. Young people discover their talents and pursue careers that can be roughly divided into either the sciences (the study of the structure and behavior of the physical and natural world through observation and experiment) or the humanities (the study of human culture such as language, literature, philosophy, religion, history, and art). Their choice is likely to depend on their comfort level with quantitative areas such as mathematics. But once they decide, they find their education quickly veering off in one direction, often to the exclusion of all other subjects. This is unfortunate since life's big questions beg for input from all areas of thought. Both science and the humanities have important things to say about human origins, for example. And solving the riddle of human origins appears to be the key to answering many of our biggest questions.

Near the middle of the twentieth century, British scientist and novelist C. P. Snow described the disconnect between science and the humanities in his now famous book, *The Two Cultures and the Scientific Revolution*. He wrote that the intellectual life of all of Western society is split into these two cultures (science and the humanities) that have a terrible time trying to communicate with each other, and that this is a major hindrance in solving the world's problems.[1] The tragedy here is that we need these, and all, fields of study to be in productive dialogue, not only to help solve the world's problems, but also to help answer life's biggest questions. It may turn out that these two objectives are very much related.

In the mid-1990s, writer John Brockman asserted the ascendency and predominance of science by publishing provocative interviews with several big-name scientists in his book, *The Third Culture: Beyond the Scientific Revolution*. These scientists had been successful at popularizing their work by writing in a manner that captured the attention and imagination of the public.[2] In a sense, they represented a new integration of science and the humanities, since they were able to harness the power of captivating literature to promote scientific research and discovery.

More recently, psychologist Jerome Kagan, in his book, *The Three Cultures: Natural Sciences, Social Sciences, and the Humanities in the 21st Century*, argues that a third culture (the social sciences such as sociology, political science, economics, psychology, and anthropology) has emerged. He helps to explain why all of these cultures have difficulty talking to each other, but emphasizes that each makes important contributions to our understanding of human nature. He concludes, for example, that the evidence from all three cultures has led him to question the popular belief that human behavior is mainly determined by biological processes.[3] This is an important example of how multiple fields of knowledge illuminate our understanding of humanity, which helps us answer some of life's biggest questions.

Engineering Joins the Conversation

In fact, it is the social science of psychology that originally birthed the concept of **affordance** (a relationship that provides a capability), which is featured as one of the key ideas of this book. Engineering researchers have recently claimed that affordance is the underlying and unifying principle in engineering and technology.[4] The reader must have patience at this point because the history and usefulness of affordances are explained in detail in a future chapter. For now, allow me to continue with how the field of engineering might assist in facilitating healthy interdisciplinary dialogue.

A *fourth* culture, consisting of engineering and technology, has adopted the concept of affordances to help clarify the intricacies of product design and reverse engineering (disassembling something to figure out how it works). As evident from the subtitle of this book, another key idea is that the field of engineering has important points to contribute to these conversations. Engineering is often confused with science, or taken to be one of the sciences, but this is an incorrect view that clouds an important distinction. While science is knowledge of the physical world gained through observation and experimentation, engineering is the practical application of this knowledge to solve problems or create affordances (i.e., expand peoples' capabilities by recognizing and implementing key relationships).

Like the popular science writers of Brockman's book, *The Third Culture*, engineers are also in the business of bringing scientific discoveries to the public, not in literary form, but in physical form, by way of useful products. In this manner, engineering already serves as a kind of mediator between science and the general public. Engineers learn of a scientific discovery and ponder the question, "What do we make of this?" Indeed, this question can be considered in both a literal sense and a figurative sense. Engineers earn their "bread and butter" by physically devising a valuable product based on scientific principles. But engineers with a more philosophical bent find themselves wondering how scientific discoveries impact life's big questions. This naturally leads to the potential for engineering to function as an intermediary between science and the humanities in addressing these questions. Perhaps it's time to make room at the table for a fourth culture: engineering and technology (see Figure 1–1).

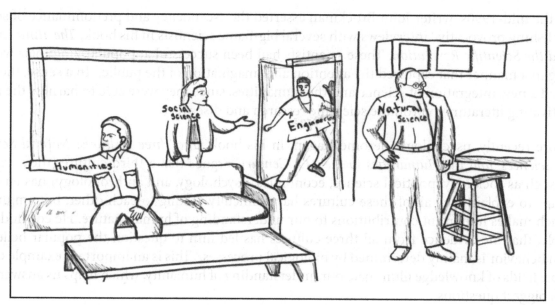

Figure 1–1   Engineering Makes an Entrance[5]

Contributed by Wyatt Bullard © Kendall Hunt Publishing Company

Background on the Conflict between Science and Religion

One subdiscipline of humanities that seems to be in continual conflict with science is religion, especially on the issue of human origins. Science has been very successful recently in helping us understand the order and mechanisms in nature that characterize living systems. But this success in expanding our scientific understanding is not achieved at the exclusion or minimization of religious beliefs. Just because we have a scientific explanation for a particular phenomenon doesn't mean God is not involved, either directly or indirectly. On the contrary, aspects of nature such as reliability, order, complexity, harmony, and beauty have often been recognized as having significance for religious belief. The existence and elegance of highly mathematical natural laws that result in complex organisms such as human beings speaks in favor of the surpassing ingenuity and expertise of a law-giving Mastermind behind the universe.

But books like biologist Richard Dawkins' *The God Delusion*[6] paint distorted pictures of science and religion that unnecessarily bring them into conflict. He and other "new atheists" seem to write in order to convince people that religious faith is unreasonable if one is scientifically enlightened. Having taught engineering at a Christian university for twenty-seven years and spoken with many students and parents about these issues, it is clear that this kind of polemic material also has the effect of discouraging young people from pursuing studies in science and engineering. Most people naturally tend to avoid conflict, and the idea that science and faith don't mix provides one more reason for the spiritually-minded to choose a non-technical major in college.

In his book *Where the Conflict Really Lies,* philosopher Alvin Plantinga argues persuasively that it is not science and religion that are necessarily in conflict, but rather the worldviews of naturalism and theism.[7] Theologian Alister McGrath agrees with this assessment as described in his book, *Science and Religion: A New Introduction.* These works help to dispel the myth of perpetual conflict between science and religion that seems to be so prominently promoted by the popular media.

McGrath traces the history of the current conflict back to the social conditions of Victorian England. With the gradual establishment of a new social group made up of professional scientists, competition arose with many of the clergy, who had traditionally practiced science at the amateur level. As the professionals sought to distance themselves from their amateur colleagues, academic culture and academic freedom called for separation of science and religion. Thus, it was only a small step to depict the church as an opponent of science education.[8]

The idea that science and religion just can't go together is still propagated today by many on both sides, due largely to fear or ignorance of the other side's position. However, survey data indicate that the conflict model might not be as pervasive as the popular media often suggests. A recent study by sociologist Elaine Howard Ecklund at Rice University found that nearly 70 percent of evangelical Christians do not view science and religion as being in conflict with each other.[9] It is hoped that this book might further advance this perspective, and provide some measure of reconciliation between proponents of extreme positions in both science and religion.

Some of the controversy can immediately be defused simply by providing a better understanding of the definitions and limitations of both science and religion. Science is knowledge of the physical world gained through observation and experimentation,[10] and as such, it is limited in what it can tell us. Since it is restricted to the physical world, science cannot prove or disprove the existence of God, for example, although it does provide evidence that bears on this question. But science cannot really "prove" anything in the strict sense of the word, because additional evidence only increases our confidence that a particular understanding of nature is correct.

Religion is a set of beliefs concerning the nature of the universe, especially when considered as a supernatural creation, usually involving ritual observances, and often containing a moral code governing human conduct.[11] There are many religions in the world and they can be very different from each other, so we should take care to be more specific when using this term. Religions are often based on revealed knowledge (sacred writings such as the Bible), as well as scientific and other forms of knowledge. Therefore, religion is also very limited in its ability to answer questions of a scientific nature.

Young People Wrestle with Science and Faith

With these definitions for science and religion, it is easy to see that conflict can arise if the revealed knowledge appears to contradict what we know from science or any other field of observable knowledge. This is how most of the conflict between science and religion originates. Even within the church, there is a lot of conflict on these issues. In his book *You Lost Me: Why Young Christians are Leaving Church . . . and Rethinking Faith*, David Kinnaman, president of the Barna Group, devotes an entire chapter to how his survey data reveals a church that is perceived to be "anti-science," especially by youths with a Christian background. Kinnaman reports that 52 percent of youth group teens in one survey aspired to science-related careers (medical and health professions, engineering, science, technology, and veterinary medicine), but only 1 percent of their youth pastors addressed issues of science in the past year.[12]

Another Barna survey of 18- to 29-year-olds with a Christian background provides an interesting confession of their thoughts on these issues.

- ▶ 52% agreed that Christians are too confident that they know all the answers.

- ▶ 41% agreed that churches are out of step with the scientific world in which we live.

- ▶ 34% agreed that Christianity is anti-science.

- ▶ 29% agreed that Christianity makes complex things too simple.

- ▶ 26% agreed that Christianity is anti-intellectual.

- ▶ And 34% agreed that they have been turned off by the creation-versus-evolution debate.[13]

I suspect part of the reason why youth are turned off is due to the atmosphere of a debate, which tends to produce more heat than light. Dialogue, where participants listen carefully to strive for understanding of the other's situation,[14] may be a better option than focusing intently on how best to defeat an opponent in an argument.

Kinnaman claims that the church is losing too many young scientists. He tells the story of a "young science-minded prodigal" named Mike, who was raised to believe in God, but became an atheist in high school. Mike agreed to speak at a pastor's seminar to help Christian leaders understand why young people are falling away from the faith. He shared, "It was tenth grade. I started learning about evolution. It felt like my first window into the real world. To be honest, I think that learning about science was the straw that broke the camel's back. I knew from church that I couldn't believe in both science and God, so that was it. I didn't believe in God anymore."[15]

It's sad that Mike's understanding of science and religion culminated in his need to choose between these two options, as if they are mutually exclusive. His assertion that the church was responsible for his "either-or" mentality is a stinging indictment. Even so, I would not agree that the church is primarily at fault in this case. Certainly, the responsibility for rejecting the truth of God's existence lies squarely on Mike's shoulders. But one of the sobering realities about living in a fallen world is this: There is plenty of blame to go around. And perhaps the church can do a better job of helping people reconcile issues in science and religion.

The irony here is that the Bible teaches that aspects of nature actually declare the glory of God (Psalm 19:1), and the study of nature in general provides unmistakable, though limited, knowledge of God (Romans 1:20). And yet, young people in particular appear to be picking up the idea that belief in God and valuing the study of nature are somehow incompatible. I regard this as one of the most tragic and pressing problems in the church today. It is a misconception that must be brought to light and dispelled if the church is to remain relevant in a global society that is not only saturated, but also enamored, with science and technology.

This book is not an attempt to "prove" God's existence from the findings of nature. Just because everyone has some knowledge of God, though they may try to suppress it (Romans 1:18), doesn't mean that his existence can be compellingly demonstrated from one person to another, like a line-upon-line mathematical proof. Rather, this work is an attempt to show that what have become known as the STEM fields (science, technology, engineering, and mathematics), with a particular emphasis on engineering, have much to contribute to our understanding of God and how he is choosing to "run this show." I think concepts from the field of engineering have great potential for helping us make sense of the history and current state of the universe.

Hope for Reconciliation

I make these assertions with some measure of confidence since I have been teaching engineering at a Christian university for over a quarter of a century, and have had considerable firsthand experience with how students are wrestling with these issues. In the last ten years, my research interests have shifted to include the relationship between science and religion, and the role of engineering in this conversation. I have made hundreds of presentations in churches and schools on these topics, and have received a lot of feedback. I direct a team of undergraduate students who conduct research in these areas, and they are very effective at helping me understand the issues from their generation's perspective.

We have recently completed a four-year grant project to translate information from the academy to the church in an effort to help Christians reconcile science and religion. Survey data from this project indicate that seminars based on the information in this book have been effective in achieving multiple objectives: This information helps people understand problems in science and faith. It increases enthusiasm for science and engineering. It helps people appreciate the ingenuity that underlies our universe. It increases understanding of evolutionary biology as it relates to Christian faith. It helps people better understand the Bible's creation accounts. And most importantly, it deepens their knowledge of God, and enhances their relationship with him.[16] Therefore, I am very excited and hopeful that this information will find a larger audience, and have a greater impact, in book form.

Although Plantinga and McGrath rightly point out that there is no *inherent* conflict between science and religion, there is conflict nonetheless. One aspect of this conflict is the apparent disagreement between the special revelation of Scripture, and the general revelation of nature. The Bible is referred to as the special revelation of God because it was uniquely delivered to particular peoples at particular times, while nature is considered the general revelation of God due to its general availability to all people throughout history.

Philosopher Thomas K. Johnson brings another aspect of this conflict to light in his book *The First Step in Missions Training: How our Neighbors are Wrestling with God's General Revelation*. He believes that the first step in training for Christian missions is to orient workers to the internal conflict that everyone endures because of their tendency to suppress the general revelation of God. He writes, "The central internal conflict within human life is that of both knowing God and not knowing God at the same time because, without the gospel of Christ, people usually repress and attempt to avoid God's general revelation which is filled with rich, complex content."[17]

Christians need to realize that even before they speak to people about God, someone has already been speaking to them. They have been hearing God's voice in nature. And God has engineered the universe in such a manner that his "eternal power and divine nature" are communicated to everyone (Romans 1:20). In reality, the universe has been set up to facilitate recognition of the need for repentance and redemption. It's time for Christians to recognize what God is doing in revealing himself through the realm of nature, and look to help people resolve their conflicts when it comes to the general revelation. I believe this is an important step on the journey toward laying aside our own ideas for personal salvation, and trusting in God's well-engineered redemptive plan. In addition, when conflict is approached with the right attitude, it will often result in something good, as will be seen in the conclusion of the story that began this chapter.

SEEDS OF CONFLICT BEAR FRUIT OF HUMBLE PIE

As I sat there wondering how to respond to Father Vernon's penetrating question ("So then, where *did* you get the alcohol?"), I stared out the window, and into the large lawn in front of the school. I played pick-up football games on that lawn, and it reminded me of playing football in our side yard at home as a young boy. One of my favorite things to do was to run with the ball, and try to elude my older brothers during regular tackle football games. I would pretend to be some great football star that I had just seen on TV in slow motion and set to music with mesmerizing narration by John Facenda, who had become known as the "Voice of God" for his dramatic voice-overs for NFL Films Incorporated.

When my brothers would agree to a game, I would fly out the back door, streak across the patio and dive into the grass to help prepare myself for the hits I was about to endure. Little did I know at the time, but the force of those carefully measured tackles were calibrated to ensure that I suffered no serious injuries. On days like that it seemed as if I didn't have a care in the world. Everything was so much simpler then. Now things had gotten very complicated, very quickly.

I was still staring out the window as Father Vernon's next words rang sharply in my ears, arresting my momentary daydream, "Answer the question. Where did you get the alcohol?" Still at a loss for what to say, I noticed the group of large evergreen trees on the front lawn, and a simple fabrication began to assemble itself in my mind. I offered a dubious alternate account, "After the football game, I met some people out front by those trees and they gave me the alcohol."

"Did you know these people?" asked the good Father.

"No, I just met them," I said.

"Who were they? What are their names?" he said.

"I don't know," I replied, hoping my unlikely story would stick, and we could just get all this behind us. There was a long silence and Father Vernon seemed dumbfounded and uncertain about what to ask next. Eventually, after a few more unsuccessful attempts to gain additional information, he dismissed me from his office, informing me that I would soon learn of the consequences I would incur for my irresponsible behavior. Although I felt relieved that the questioning was over, I was a bit nervous about what my punishment might be. I had good reason to be nervous.

I was a nerd who loved to engage in athletics; a strange combination of sport smarts and quirky quickness, but small of stature, with microscopic muscles. Even so, I was bound and determined not to let my slight 125-pound frame stand in the way of a career as a college or even professional football or basketball star. That was the dream to which I was desperately clinging, and it was about to slip even further from my grasp. I soon learned that, although I had not been expelled from school, I had been put on probation for the rest of the academic year.

I knew what this meant, and it was a devastating blow. No more football! No more basketball! No more pole-vaulting, long-jumping, or high-jumping for an entire year! How would I ever get caught back up after a whole year off from athletics? The coaches were sympathetic to my plight, and with their help, I was able to convince the administration to allow me to at least participate in practice sessions, even though I couldn't be at the games. Still, it was a very bitter pill to swallow, but that was not the worst of it.

With only about 75 students in the graduating class, our high school was among the smallest in Indiana, and everybody knew what had happened on that fateful night at the homecoming dance. I found that I had instantly become a reluctant celebrity. I was quite ashamed of what I had done, not so much because I had embarrassed my family, but mainly because of my extended disqualification from athletic competition. I wanted to crawl under a rock, but for the next several weeks, there was no place to hide from the continual barrage of jokes about my newly-found "love for drinking."

Although it has been more than forty years ago now, I still remember many of them. A senior girl who I didn't know well, but admired very much, and who worked behind the lunch counter, handed me a carton of milk and said, "Is this strong enough for you?" In the middle of my chorus class, a group of my buddies spontaneously broke into a rousing rendition of "WHAT SHALL WE DO WITH A DRUNKEN HALSMER!" Even my English teacher, who regularly called on students to recite the definitions of the day's vocabulary words, intentionally called on me to give the definition of the word "imbibe." I know these all seem like little things, but they were beginning to accumulate on top of my psyche, like I was being buried under a pile of filthy stinking laundry. Was this the person I had become? A drunk! At least lots of people seemed to think so.

My English teacher must have sensed the quaver in my faltering voice as I responded, "to drink," because he immediately asked me to join him for a private meeting out in the hallway. As he closed the door behind us, he asked me in a sincere voice if I minded him joking with me in this way. My eyes were welling up with tears, but I was pretending to be a man, so I fought hard to suppress the truth, and said, "No, everybody else is doing it." I'm certain that he saw right through my fragile façade, because he apologized anyway, and then we went back in to finish class. I didn't know what else to do besides just try to endure the joking, and view it as friendly kidding around, but it was extremely humbling.

After a year or two as I looked back on the traumatic events of that fall semester, I came to realize that they had changed me significantly. Prior to that fateful Friday night, nearly everything had been going my way. Success with grades, sports, and friends had made me prideful and overconfident. I should have remembered that pride comes before a fall (Proverbs 16:18). I was a loudmouth who was quick to speak because I saw myself as being so clever and funny. I thought I could do most anything, and get away with it. I guess that partly explains my naïve and outrageous behavior that night. In a way, I was drunk on success, until I literally got drunk over-celebrating, and everything changed.

But the more I thought about it, the more I began to realize that the change was actually for the better. Sure, I lost a year of athletic competition, but let's face it, with my physique, or lack thereof, I was not destined for the NFL or the NBA. I turned out to be the consummate late-bloomer, and have enjoyed competitive athletics much more in my later years than I ever did as a youngster. Furthermore, without a commitment to varsity athletics in college, I was able to devote additional energies to my studies, which eventually resulted in a doctorate in mechanical engineering from UCLA, and more recently, a master of arts in biblical literature from Oral Roberts University.

But the really significant change was to my spirit. I was so humbled and humiliated by these sobering events that my attitude, and resulting behavior, immediately changed. I did a lot less talking, and a lot more listening and thinking. My overconfidence was replaced by a serious understanding of how stupid I could be when left to my own devices. Needless to say, I was a lot more careful about drinking alcohol and handling peer pressure. And I was a lot more thankful for what I had, and for the chance to improve myself.

They say that you don't know what you've got until it's taken away from you. After losing a year of sports, and almost losing the privilege of attending that excellent Catholic high school, I came to realize what wonderful opportunities I had been given in life. And finally, I ended up in a place where I was better able to receive what I needed from God, because God resists the proud, but gives grace to the humble (James 4:6). By no means was God finished with me yet, but I now see those events as a significant turning point on a road that continues to lead towards him, even if in a somewhat zig-zag manner at times. It's curious to me that a period of so much conflict, and what I perceived at the time to be loss, could result in such positive outcomes. This is a recurring theme in this book, and in the universe, which will be explored further in the next chapter.

STUDY QUESTIONS

1. Describe times in your life when you experienced conflict or other forms of adversity.
2. How have your experiences of adversity changed you? Either positively or negatively.
3. What "big questions" are you most curious about? How have you tried to answer them?
4. Are you more drawn to the sciences? Or to the humanities? Why?
5. Why do you think the sciences and the humanities have trouble communicating with each other?
6. How might the field of engineering mediate communication between the sciences and the humanities?
7. Give several examples of how engineers recognize and arrange relationships to create new affordances.
8. How do the laws of mathematics and the laws of nature bear on the question of God's existence?
9. Do you think science and religion are necessarily in conflict? Why or why not?
10. In what ways are both science and religion limited understandings of reality?
11. If there is no inherent conflict between science and religion, then where does the conflict really reside?
12. Summarize how a large segment of young Christians view the science/faith conflict.
13. Why might *dialogue* on science and faith issues be more productive than *debates*?
14. What objectives have been furthered through presentation of the information in this book?
15. Compare and contrast the two forms of revelation God employs.

ENDNOTES

1. C. P. Snow, *The Two Cultures and the Scientific Revolution* (Cambridge: Cambridge University Press, 1960).
2. John Brockman, *The Third Culture: Beyond the Scientific Revolution* (New York: Touchstone, 1996).
3. Jerome Kagan, *The Three Cultures: Natural Sciences, Social Sciences, and the Humanities in the 21st Century* (Cambridge: Cambridge University Press, 2009).
4. J. R. A. Maier and G. M. Fadel, "Affordance: The Fundamental Concept in Engineering Design," *Proceedings of the ASME Design Engineering TecÚical Conference 4* (2001): 177–86.
5. Illustration provided by Wyatt Bullard. Did you notice a resemblance to a popular TV show?
6. Richard Dawkins, *The God Delusion* (New York: Houghton Mifflin, 2006).
7. Alvin Plantinga, *Where the Conflict Really Lies: Science, Religion, and Naturalism* (New York: Oxford University Press, 2011).

8. Alister E. McGrath, *Science and Religion: A New Introduction* (West Sussex, UK: Wiley-Blackwell, 2009).

9. Rice University, "Nearly 70 percent of evangelicals do not view religion, science as being in conflict," ScienceDaily. www.sciencedaily.com/releases/2015/03/150313110432.htm.

10. www.dictionary.com

11. www.dictionary.com

12. David Kinnaman, *You Lost Me: Why Young Christians are Leaving Church . . . and Rethinking Faith* (Grand Rapids, MI: Baker, 2011), 140.

13. Kinnaman, *You Lost Me,* 137.

14. Maggie Herzig and Laura Chasin, *Fostering Dialogue Across Divides: A Nuts and Bolts Guide from the Public Conversations Project* (Watertown, MA: Public Conversations Project, 2006), 3.

15. Kinnaman, *You Lost Me,* 138.

16. Dominic Halsmer, Lanny Endicott, Caleb Lutz, Joshua Williams, Emily Dzurilla, and Alex Mills, "Sailing the Seas to Scientific Literacy without Shipwrecking Faith in America's Bible Belt," *International Journal of Science in Society 7, no. 2* (2015): 25–36.

17. Thomas K. Johnson, *The First Step in Missions Training: How our Neighbors are Wrestling with God's General Revelation* (Hamburg, Culture and Science Publications, 2014), 30.

CHAPTER TWO

The Potential for Unity in Diversity

CAN WE TALK ABOUT EVOLUTION?

It was about a year after I started teaching engineering at Oral Roberts University in 1992 that my dad went on to be with his Maker. In the last several years of his life, he and my mom had a heart for increased unity among Christians, and they were actively working toward that goal in our hometown of Lafayette, Indiana. They raised us kids in the Catholic faith, but during my elementary school days, they experienced a dynamic spiritual renewal that rocked our religious worldviews, nearly shaking the beads right off our rosaries.

For several years I resisted their invitation to pursue a more personal relationship with Jesus Christ, but near the end of my undergraduate degree at Purdue University, two things had convinced me to give up the fight. The first was my realization that the pleasures of this world were fleeting, and unable to provide true satisfaction. The second, and more potent reason for my conversion, was the change I had seen in my parents' lives. They exhibited the love and joy that Jesus said would characterize the lives of his followers. Only later would I dig deeper, and uncover the interesting relationship between science and the Christian faith, with its accompanying additional reasons to believe.

So it was with great excitement, as I was finishing my doctoral degree in mechanical engineering at UCLA, that I read that ORU was looking to hire an assistant professor in mechanical engineering. I fondly remembered my parents watching Oral Roberts' healing programs on TV when I was little. Now I was in a position to really contribute full-time to this powerful ministry, and perhaps take some free courses in theology at the same time. I had already come to realize that I needed more theological training if I was going to seriously address my newly discovered passion: problems in science and faith.

I started taking courses toward a master of arts in biblical literature as soon as I joined the university, but we were working hard to get the engineering program accredited at that time, and my darling wife, Kate, and I had four small children. I remember her asking me, kindly, but with a hint of fatigue in her voice, "Are you sure this is the right season of our lives for you to be pursuing another degree?" Although I was reluctant to admit it, this gently probing question was just what I needed to hear. After realizing how overcommitted I had become, I put the masters degree on hold until our youngest was near high school age. Then, after only twenty years and with a great sense of accomplishment, I finally finished the biblical literature degree in May of 2013. That would turn out to be a year of tremendous testing, but not because of this additional graduate degree.

It was the summer of 2012 when I was developing a proposal for a new Center for Faith and Learning at ORU. I had been the dean of the College of Science and Engineering for five years, and that stint in administration helped me to see the need for an office to promote the further integration of Christian worldview into every academic area of the university. After joining ORU in 1992, it hadn't taken me long to become fully committed to the mission of the university, and I felt at home among faculty and administrators, as if we were all family. In a very real sense, we were family. It was the fulfillment of a dream I had envisioned as a child: to teach at a unique school with my brothers and sisters where we could make learning relevant and fun.

During that same summer of 2012, I also became aware of an exciting opportunity to apply for a three-year grant from the BioLogos Foundation to help Christians reconcile issues in science and faith; in particular, the biggest issue of our era: how to think about biological evolution and human origins. I felt like this was the kind of project for which I had been preparing for so long. It was a chance to help Christians better understand key issues with regard to origins, to carry forward my parents' vision for unity on these divisive issues, and also to provide a concrete example of integration in faith and learning for the new center. But as I began to prepare the grant application and gather a multidisciplinary team of faculty from theology and the sciences, I also began to realize that there was serious concern among some of the faculty about whether or not this project was in the best interests of the university.

Although BioLogos is a group of self-proclaimed Christians, the concern was based on their view of creation. According to their mission statement, "BioLogos invites the church and the world to see the harmony between science and biblical faith as we present an evolutionary understanding of God's creation."[1] Their website provides more detail on what this implies. For example, "We believe that the diversity and interrelation of all life on earth are best explained by the God-ordained process of evolution with common descent. Thus, evolution is not in opposition to God, but a means by which God providentially achieves his purposes. Therefore, we reject ideologies that claim that evolution is a purposeless process or that evolution replaces God."[2]

Thus, some members of the faculty and administration were concerned that if ORU accepted a grant from BioLogos, ORU could be viewed as holding the same positions as BioLogos. This would not sit well with some of our constituents, and ORU might suffer a drop in enrollment as a result. Although ORU has never taken an official position on the details about how God made human beings, this was still a very legitimate concern which had to be addressed.

Before the full project proposal was developed and sent to BioLogos, a meeting was held with the president of ORU, the project team, and the concerned faculty and administrators. The issues were discussed and the decision was made to proceed with the proposal. The reasoning was simply that the receipt of a grant does not necessarily imply agreement on all issues between the parties involved. It was recognized in that meeting that Oral Roberts himself often received donations from people with whom he didn't necessarily see eye-to-eye. Furthermore, the desperate need for education on science and faith issues, especially among young people in the local church, was generally acknowledged and appreciated.

With this vote of confidence, I set about the task of finalizing the project proposal titled, "Science and the Wisdom of God: An Interdisciplinary Project to Help Christians Gain an Appreciation for the Ingenuity Behind our Evolving Universe." I attempted to make use of my engineering expertise in crafting a project that would place the theories of stellar and biological evolution as possibilities for Christians to carefully consider, within the larger context of a scientifically informed history of an ingeniously engineered universe, but also in light of the special revelation of Scripture.

The proposal received all the appropriate administrative approvals and was submitted to the BioLogos Foundation for evaluation. In December of 2012, out of 225 initial applications, and 86 invited full proposals, the ORU project was selected as 1 of 37 that would receive funding from BioLogos. I remember reading the congratulatory email on my computer at home over Christmas break. I threw back my chair, jumped up in the air, and knocked my heels together! It was just a little something my dad used to do when he was in a celebratory mood. He called it "cutting the mustard."

Upon returning from break with the good news, my elation was soon tempered by reports that opposition to the project had resurfaced, and that we might be asked to decline the awarded grant. We had another meeting with administrators where the president asked us how strongly we felt about keeping the grant. Somewhat sheepishly, I said that we would be very disappointed if we were not allowed to retain the grant and conduct the project. I soon regretted that I did not speak in a more assertive manner to defend the importance of our project in that meeting.

Prior to these events, being forceful and commanding in such settings did not come naturally or easily to me, given my personality type. I didn't like conflict, and I was beginning to doubt my ability to deal with all the institutional conflict that seemed to be brewing over this issue. I confess that, at the time, I was also having second thoughts about being able to complete the large amount of work to which we had committed in the proposal. I'm afraid these doubts might have been inadvertently communicated to those in the meeting, and it was quickly decided that the matter should be taken before the faculty in a special meeting to gauge their opinion.

A few days later, the faculty of the College of Science and Engineering, the College of Theology and Ministry, and the College of Nursing, along with a few other interested faculty and administrators, met for a one-hour meeting to hear about the project and discuss its feasibility. Here is another point at which I must confess my sins. I had intended that I and the four team members would each have a few minutes to summarize our parts of the project, after which we would take questions from the audience. However, I did not lay out a detailed schedule, and there had been no communication with the administration about how much of the hour would consist of input from the audience.

I opened the meeting with an overview of the project that went longer than I anticipated, and was soon being requested to take questions and comments from the audience. I objected that the rest of the team had not yet presented, but it was insisted that the feedback begin immediately. It was only then that I began to realize the full extent of the opposition to this project. Detractors rose one by one to express their objections. I had decided ahead of time that I would not respond to the objections because I wanted to allow more time for the audience to speak. I simply thanked each speaker for their input and went on to the next one. Not all of the comments were negative, but the majority were.

By the end of the meeting, it was obvious that several faculty and administrators were strongly opposed to our reception of the grant. Furthermore, my decision not to respond to their objections gave the impression that there *were* no good responses. I looked over and saw the terrible disappointment on the faces of my team members. As the meeting came to a close, one of the more outspoken members of the team stood up and summarized what we all were probably thinking, "Well, that's the end of that."

I was devastated. I had tried to share my excitement with my faculty family about the potential for this project to bring unity and reconciliation, but instead it was seen as a dangerous harbinger of strife and division. And I felt that it was largely my fault. I began to wonder if I was cut out to lead this kind of project. A few days later, an online vote was taken which confirmed my fearful suspicion that a majority of faculty and administrators from the colleges in attendance at the meeting were opposed to the grant. It seemed as if this grant, and my dream of a funded project to help Christians understand science and faith issues, was dead on arrival . . . but sometimes that which is dead may live again.

Putting Together the Worldview Puzzle

How do people come to such different conclusions when forming their worldviews? We all experience the same world, don't we? Well, yes and no. While it's true that we all reside on the same planet, the local culture and family environment can have a big influence on a person's worldview. A worldview is basically how you see the world; your accumulated knowledge of how the world works and what it's all about. Humanity is fortunate to have a great variety of cultures that all address the questions of worldview. Each person has their own worldview, but it is shaped and influenced by the people they meet, with their various understandings of reality.

This is beneficial because forming a worldview is like putting together the pieces of a jigsaw puzzle. It's always good to have more people helping because everyone looks at the puzzle a little differently, and has their own contribution to make. Some like to work on the edges first, while others may choose to focus on pieces of a particular color or object. But before long, they're making connections with each other and the whole puzzle starts coming together.

For this reason, it's important to maintain an open mind when it comes to your worldview. You may think that you already have a pretty good understanding of reality, but worldviews should never be considered finished or complete, because humanity learns so much more every day. We should strive to keep learning throughout our entire lives, and continue to refine our worldviews.

A person's worldview typically takes shape based on various life experiences such as formal education and personal relationships. But people generally don't think much about their worldview. They tend to lose sight of the forest for the trees. That is, they get so bogged down in the details of their lives that they tend to ignore the big questions involving overall worldview. Sometimes they establish a particular worldview early in their lives and try to force-fit any newly learned information into an old and outdated worldview.

Many peoples' worldviews are established, or significantly modified, during their educational experiences, because this is when they receive a huge influx of information from diverse fields and meet many new and interesting people. It may seem as though one person's worldview is as good as another's; who are we to judge someone else's view of reality? Of course everyone is entitled to their own worldview, but the accuracy of a worldview can actually be tested, and holding an inaccurate worldview can be dangerous to your health. If someone didn't believe in or appreciate the "gravity" of the law of gravity, for example, they would certainly regret the horrifying consequences of walking off a cliff. So it's not a bad idea to test your worldview and try to get a sense of how it measures up to reality.

How to Test a Worldview

The purpose of this section is to discuss the value and method of testing a worldview to see how well it matches with reality. A further purpose is to propose and support the idea that an "engineering mindset" is particularly applicable to the accurate formation and testing of a worldview. Engineers are in the business of gathering diverse pieces of information and trying to make some practical sense of it all. Typically this results in the synthesis of some complex device or system that makes extensive use of the laws of nature.

Thus, engineers understand how the world works to a substantial degree, and they make use of this knowledge in an attempt to improve the human condition. Furthermore, engineers often find themselves engaged in the reverse process, in which they carefully dissect an existing device or system in order to learn its secrets, or discover how it is supposed to work. This process, which is known as reverse engineering, is actually a microcosm of our ongoing effort to understand all that we can about ourselves and the universe in which we live.

According to philosopher Kenneth Samples' book, *A World of Difference*, there are six major components that make up the conceptual heart of any worldview. They are:

1. **Theology**—Concept of God, or absence of deity.
2. **Metaphysics**—View of external reality, especially the origin and significance of the cosmos.
3. **Epistemology**—Study of the origin, nature, limits, and validity of knowledge.
4. **Axiology**—Study of the origin, nature, meaning, and criteria of values.
5. **Anthropology**—Study of the origin, nature, problems, and destiny of human beings.
6. **History**—Study of the nature, direction, and purpose of unfolding historical events.[3]

These are the most important categories of knowledge for thinking about the world, its meaning, and basically how it works. A person's collection of beliefs in these areas will determine thinking, motivation, and behavior, making it of critical importance for living a successful life.

For the purpose of evaluating a worldview, Samples also suggests the following nine tests:

1. **Coherence**—Is it logically consistent?
2. **Balance**—Is it appropriately balanced between simplicity and complexity?
3. **Power & Scope**—How well does it explain and how wide is the range of explanation?
4. **Correspondence**—Does it correspond to empirical facts and human experience?
5. **Verification**—Can the central truth-claims be verified or falsified?
6. **Pragmatic**—Does it promote relevant, practical, and workable results?
7. **Existential**—Does it address the internal needs, desires, and aspirations of humanity?
8. **Cumulative**—Is it supported by multiple lines of converging evidence?
9. **Competitive**—Can it successfully compete in the marketplace of ideas?[4]

Scientists and engineers typically have a very high regard for truth because they daily experience the value, indeed the profitability, of having an accurate representation of physical reality. However, they also understand that their representations are probably not perfect. Engineers are especially in-tune with the idea that full and complete knowledge of all aspects of a project need not be attained before decisions are made to finalize a "good-enough" design, and get the product "out the door."

Samples confirms this same idea with regard to worldview decisions when he writes, "No worldview is perfect in explaining reality. Instead, a worldview functions much like a scientific model in its attempt to provide a broad and general explanatory theory about reality. Lack of perfection should not prevent anyone from evaluating various positions and embracing the one that scores highest on the nine critical tests."[5] To one degree or another, we all evaluate our own worldviews using these tests, but we should keep in mind the dangers of egocentric and socio-centric thinking to the process of critical thinking. Egocentric thinking is our tendency to "not naturally appreciate the point of view of others, nor the limitations in our own point of view."[6] Socio-centric thinking is a similar pitfall, but with regard to groups instead of individuals. It is the uncritical tendency to place our own culture, nation, or religion above all others.[7]

But the caution to avoid uncritical egocentric and socio-centric thinking should be balanced with the realization that one worldview may indeed score higher on the nine tests than others. Furthermore, an overemphasis on critical thinking may lead to intellectual paralysis, where one is unable to make appropriate worldview decisions due to an overwhelming and unhealthy fear of error.[8] Samples provides an interesting example by submitting historic Christianity to each of these tests.[9] In his opinion, "The broad Christian theistic perspective . . . shows itself to be the most reasonable explanation of life and reality. [It] supplies a rational hope to all people wrestling with the questions of life."[10]

Philosopher Nancy Pearcey, in her book *Finding Truth*, also encourages testing to expose false reductionism in several popular worldviews of our time. She argues those worldviews which reject God inevitably set up an idol that always leads to a lower view of human life.[11] According to Pearcey, not only do these idol-centered worldviews often contradict what we know about the world, but they also contradict themselves by reducing the activity of the human mind to something less than true reason.

For example, someone may promote relativism, which claims that there is no universal truth. But that statement itself makes a universal claim, which becomes self-defeating by contradicting itself.[12]

While these books by Samples and Pearcey make a strong case for a Christian worldview, Christians should be careful not to project the idea that they have all the answers. Study of the human condition, along with lessons from the history of science and mathematics, indicates the existence of very real limits on human knowledge and capabilities, as discussed in the next section.

Limits on Human Knowledge

The power and profitability of science in our day is seen in the myriad of technological devices that assist us in our everyday lives. The predominance of science and technology has led some to suggest that even human values can be determined by science.[13] But this appears to exceed the limits of science, as it was defined earlier, and as it is commonly understood. Philosopher Brian Earp at the University of Oxford writes, "To the extent that science can 'determine' what we ought to do, it is only by providing us with empirical information, which can then be slotted into a chain of deductive (moral) reasoning. The premises of such reasoning, however, can in no way be derived from the scientific method: they come, instead, from philosophy—and common sense."[14] Indeed, one of the resounding conclusions of science in the last century is that "any scientific explanation is necessarily limited."[15]

Renowned physicist John Archibald Wheeler put it this way, "We live on an island surrounded by a sea of ignorance. As our island of knowledge grows, so does the shore of our ignorance."[16] Scientist and author Marcelo Gleiser in his book *The Island of Knowledge: The Limits of Science and the Search for Meaning* adds, "It is also good to remember that science only covers part of the island. While the physical and social sciences surely can illuminate many aspects of knowledge, they shouldn't carry the burden of having all the answers. How small a view of the human spirit to cloister all that we can achieve in one corner of knowledge! We are multidimensional creatures and search for answers in many, complementary ways. Each serves a purpose and we need them all."[17] The humanities and the sciences work in different ways and provide different aspects of truth, but each is vital to a complete and satisfying understanding of the human experience.

Even results from the field of mathematics confirm that total truth lies beyond that which human beings are able to demonstrate. Mathematician Kurt Gödel showed in his famous Incompleteness Theorem that for a complex system of axioms, there are true statements that can be formulated within the language of the system, but cannot be proved given the axioms of the system.[18] Thus the idea of *truth* cannot be reduced to the idea of *provability*.[19] Like an engineer on a tight schedule who doesn't have the time to continue to perfect a product but must get it out-the-door in the best state possible, so it seems that humans must make decisions based on a worldview that's in process and founded on limited information.

Computer scientist Noson Yanofsky summarizes our intellectual limits in *The Outer Limits of Reason: What Science, Mathematics, and Logic Cannot Tell Us*. One of the most puzzling of these limits occurs when dealing with self-referential systems. A classic example is Bertrand Russell's story of the village barber who shaves everyone who does not shave themselves. After thinking about the Barber's Paradox or other self-referential situations for a minute or two, it becomes clear that contradictions arise. Who shaves the barber? Such contradictions must be avoided for human reasoning to remain sound, and this leads to necessary limitations in our thinking.[20] Thus, any attempt to "reverse-engineer" our universe, and ultimately ourselves, as suggested later in this book, constitutes a self-referential system, and will have inherent limitations. Nevertheless, this reverse engineering approach is believed to have great potential to help in further refining our worldviews.

The Prevalence and Power of Presuppositions

Because of the limitations in human thinking and investigative capabilities, we must start our thinking processes with certain axioms, or fundamental statements that we presuppose to be true. These presuppositions end up having a tremendous influence on the conclusions we draw from the data, especially when it comes to questions of origins. Educator and author Gerald Rau highlights this point in his book, *Mapping the Origins Debate: Six Models of the Beginning of Everything*. He lays out six models of origins (from atheistic naturalism to young-earth creationism) and shows how each model presupposes an underlying philosophy that adherents take on faith. He summarizes the evidence and examines how each view assesses it in relation to the origin of the universe, the origin of life, the origin of species, and the origin of human beings.[21] These are the "big four" when it comes to origins.

Based on various assumptions about whether or not God exists, and how he might interact with the natural world, several positions have been offered to explain these origins. Rau suggests that the following six models accurately categorize the vast majority of what people believe about origins. They are:

1. **Naturalistic Evolution**—Automatic natural processes tell the whole story.
2. **Non-Teleological Evolution**—God creates but without imposing any particular purpose on an automatically deploying cosmos.
3. **Planned Evolution**—A perfect creation naturally fulfills God's purposes.
4. **Directed Evolution**—Changes in the universe and life are subtly directed over time.
5. **Old Earth Creation**—Major animal body plans were created over millions of years.
6. **Young Earth Creation**—Each animal "kind" was created in one week in the last ten thousand years.[22]

Table 2–1 on the following page provides a graphic representation of these six models with additional distinguishing features.

How did we end up with such a broad range of very different views on origins? In answering this question, Rau provides several helpful comments that also suggest a productive way forward for all who are wrestling with these issues.

According to Rau, "Although everyone has access to the same evidence, the presuppositions implicit in a person's philosophy determine the perspective from which he or she views the data, leading to different logical conclusions about which explanation best fits the evidence."[23] Basically, depending on your presuppositions, the universe is the kind of place that is somewhat open to interpretation, at least to those limited beings that reside on the planet we call Earth. Rau provides some helpful details on the various types of sciences (theoretical, experimental, observational, and historical), and the different methods they employ.

Table 2–1   Distinguishing Features of Various Origins Models (adapted from Rau)

Model	NE	NTE	PE	DE	OEC	YEC
Creator	No	Yes	Yes	Yes	Yes	Yes
Purpose	No	No	Yes	Yes	Yes	Yes
Intervention	No	No	No	Yes	Yes	Yes
Genealogy	Common descent	Common descent	Common descent	Common descent	De novo creation	De novo creation
Cosmology	Old universe	Old universe	Old universe	Old universe	Old universe	Recent creation
Process	Automatic natural processes only	Conditions necessary for life established at creation	Perfect creation naturally fulfills God's purposes	Changes in universe and life are subtly directed over time	Major body plans created over millions of years	Each "kind" created in one week, within the last 10,000 years

He reminds us that all scientific conclusions involve three things: presuppositions, logic, and evidence. And since the pertinent evidence comes from many different fields, no one person has full command of all the various lines of evidence. Thus, in following the Principle of Total Evidence (the idea that we should take everything we *collectively* know into account), we will need to learn from each other and work together.[24] The "Lone Ranger" may have been an effective approach in the Old West, but not when it comes to hacking the cosmos.

Rau also provides a nice summary of the three modes of reasoning: deductive (general to specific, leading to sure conclusions), inductive (specific to general, leading to probable conclusions), and abductive (inference to the best explanation, leading to plausible conclusions). Since models of origins are created through inductive and abductive logic, they cannot be proved to be true or false; only probable and plausible.[25] Thus the cumulative weight of the total evidence for a particular model is a key factor in deciding about origins. Philosopher Richard Swinburne takes this approach in *The Existence of God*, where he presents a compelling cumulative case for theism.[26]

But perhaps it is Rau's concluding comments that are the most valuable. As he pleads for cooperation and understanding in the midst of diversity, he writes, "Just as some of the greatest advances in science now are coming from cross-disciplinary studies, bringing together fields that previously had no interaction, so too the greatest advances in origins research will likely come from those willing to take the time and effort to combine the best work from all sides of the debate, and respond thoughtfully to opponents, rather than brushing them off as worthless."[27] It may be that all sides have something important to contribute to this conversation, and we should be listening respectfully to each other.

Two recent projects offer encouragement that Christians are overcoming divisions and working together to understand origins. Former opponents have teamed up to produce the book, *Old-Earth or Evolutionary Creation? Discussing Origins with Reasons to Believe and BioLogos.*[28] And a young earth creationist has joined forces with an evolutionary creationist to produce *The Fool and the Heretic: How Two Scientists Moved beyond Labels to a Christian Dialogue on Creation and Evolution.*[29] We should strive to respect these contributions, as we also learn to be comfortable with some uncertainty on these issues. Paul's reminder to the Corinthians is appropriate in this context. "For now we see only a reflection as in a mirror; then we shall see face to face. Now I know in part; then I shall know fully, even as I am fully known. And now these three remain: faith, hope and love. But the greatest of these is love" (1 Corinthians 13:12–13).

WHAT'S SO FUNNY 'BOUT PEACE, LOVE, AND UNDERSTANDING?[30]

Rau's work is one of the books I was reading in January and February of 2013 when confronted with opposition to the BioLogos grant. It helped me to see how reasonable people could come to such different and strongly held conclusions about origins. I also began to understand that the diversity of views on origins need not be a conversation stopper, but could serve as an opportunity to learn from each other, and grow as a community of faith. They could even model (for the larger community in and around where I live in Tulsa, Oklahoma) how a group of people could maintain a sense of family and loving unity in the midst of diverse views on origins. It occurred to me that although some heated disagreements were taking place among the faculty, at least we were openly talking about the most important science and faith issues, which is something we should have been doing a long time ago.

I think part of the reason these conversations were now able to occur was due to the recent change in organizational layout and attitude at ORU. We had recently transitioned to more of a shared-governance structure in which the faculty realized new freedoms to express their views and participate in the running of the university. The new ORU Board of Trustees chair, Mart Green, and the Green family are to be commended for initiating this change. It may ultimately prove to be of more value than the magnanimous donations they made to bring the university out of its deep and debilitating debt.

But nevertheless, after the aforementioned, discouraging faculty meeting and vote, I was perplexed at how we could possibly proceed with the project. The day after the vote came in, I remember confessing to one of my courageous team members, Andy Lang, that I couldn't see how we could move forward with the grant when so many of our "family members" seemed to be so strongly opposed to it. I was extremely disheartened that day, because that was the day I had resigned myself to relinquishing the grant. But wisdom is found in a multitude of counselors (Proverbs 15:22), and several voices (human and Otherwise) would contribute to my change of heart over the next twenty-four hours.

That same evening, I had scheduled one of the initial presentations on the BioLogos project at the monthly meeting of the Tulsa chapter of *Reasons to Believe* (a science apologetics organization based in Covina, California),[31] which was being held at the home of my friend and retired engineer, Dave Steensland. I knew many of the regular attendees at this meeting to be mature, wise, and caring people with whom I could share my heart. It's good that I was among friends that night because halfway through my PowerPoint presentation, I just ran out of emotional steam.

I guess the impact of my decision to decline the grant, which I had contemplated earlier in the day, was finally finding its full effect. I was so discouraged that it became difficult to speak. My presentation just kind of "came to a screechin' halt" (as my dad used to say) as a picture of the microwave data from the COBE satellite appeared, and remained frozen, on the screen. I remember staring out at the audience, and registering the growing concern on their faces, as the period of awkward silence just got longer and longer.

Finally, one of my old geologist friends broke in gently, saying, "That's the microwave background radiation, isn't it?" The kindness in his voice got me jump-started again, and I was able to finish the presentation. I've delivered thousands of oral presentations during my career in academia, but that's the only time I can remember struggling to finish a talk. At the end, I openly shared the situation with the grant, and my inability, thus far, to find a way forward. Sensing the importance of this project, several of the attendees offered suggestions for how a compromise might be achieved that would allow the project to proceed. Then they prayed for me. Their advice and prayers were significant, but I was still troubled about what to do.

As I was closing down the presentation on my laptop that night, someone came up behind me and began looking through the book I had brought and left on the table. The book was Kinnaman's *You Lost Me: Why Young Christians are Leaving Church . . . and Rethinking Faith*, which I briefly discussed in the first chapter. After a few moments, he slammed the book down on the table and said, "Dominic, you cannot let this go! The Church needs to hear what you've got to say." I wasn't really paying attention at the time, so I was startled, and turned around to see who was speaking. It wasn't Jesus; it was someone with a little more earthly pull (tongue-in-cheek). It was the district attorney for the City of Tulsa, Tim Harris, who is also one of the most accomplished and well respected of our ORU alumni. Being very familiar with conflict, Tim encouraged me to make attempts to try to resolve the disagreement over the grant. He also offered a powerful prayer over me and spoke words of affirmation, which I greatly appreciated, but I still couldn't see a way forward at the time; although having the support and encouragement of the Tulsa DA was no small consolation.

That night, I couldn't sleep. I had no peace about my decision to relinquish the grant. I got out of bed the next morning with the distinct impression that God was trying to tell me not to give up on the grant. Or was it my own pride, greed, and selfish ambition that was getting the best of me, and perhaps masquerading as the voice of God? I tried to weigh these possibilities as objectively as I could. As an engineer and an analytically-minded person, I typically couldn't relate very well to when Christians said they heard from God. It's not that I didn't believe them; it's just that I didn't normally or easily identify with that experience in my own life . . . until recently.

The year before all this conflict, I had experienced the distinct impression that God wanted me to volunteer as a referee for intramural basketball games at ORU. At the time, I found this to be kind of humorous because you usually hear of Christians responding to "big" callings like missions work in China or Africa; here was God, calling me to be an intramural basketball ref? I almost shrugged it off, except for one nagging reality: I didn't want to do it. Oh, I knew the game of basketball. Being from Indiana, I had played it my whole life. And there certainly was a need for better reffing in the intramural league. I had firsthand experience of that! But I didn't like conflict, or high pressure situations, and it was not easy for me to make quick decisions; all things that went along with reffing. Why did I think I should be a ref when I really didn't want to do it? It was not expected of faculty, since students typically served as referees. No great harm would come if I didn't do it.

But in the end, I could not shake the idea that somehow my Maker was communicating the idea to me. So I served as an intramural basketball ref that season. It was a humbling experience, and I made some bad calls, but overall, I was a pretty good ref. I did notice that the experience helped to further develop my leadership and decision-making skills, which was good since I was serving as Dean of the College of Science and Engineering at the time. It also improved my rapport with the students. But most importantly, after the season was over, I had the distinct impression that I had heard God's voice and obeyed, and that was extremely satisfying.

Now, as I wrestled with hearing from God about this grant, I thought back to what I had learned about hearing from God the previous year. It occurred to me that the two situations had a lot in common. There certainly was a need for the local church to receive good information on science and faith issues. And to be honest, I was not looking forward to all the conflict, hard work, pressure to perform, and decision-making that would accompany the administration of this grant. Part of me didn't want to do it, but another part of me couldn't shake the idea that God wanted us to do it; and that he was calling me to do what I could do to make it happen.

All this was rolling around in my mind the morning after that sleepless night, when after teaching a class, I ran into one of the project team members from theology. He had an idea that at first glance appeared too drastic, but upon further thought seemed like it might work. He believed that most of the opposition to the grant was coming from theology faculty, so he offered this plan: he and the other theology team member would pull out of the project and allow the grant to proceed, solely as an initiative of the College of Science and Engineering. Unfortunately, this would mean that the project would lose some of its multidisciplinary punch, but there were several faculty in science and engineering with dual-credentials in theology that could help make up for this loss, myself included.

The project team quickly met to discuss the offer, and with some reluctance, decided to pursue this as the best option. Another presentation was scheduled and delivered, this time just to the science and engineering faculty, which further described the content of seminars that would be offered to churches and Christian schools as part of the project. Another online vote of only science and engineering faculty was taken and the results indicated a slim margin in favor of retaining the grant and pursuing the project. Although this might seem to be sufficient to allow the project to go forward, the administration was still reluctant to permit it. It would take a few more weeks of negotiations and compromise before an agreement would finally be reached.

This agreement ultimately included a disclaimer on the BioLogos website, basically stating that BioLogos and its grantees do not necessarily agree on everything. In addition, the project team committed to refrain from making presentations to churches or schools with close ties to ORU in the first year of the grant. Instead, a pastor's workshop was held to obtain feedback from local clergy on how best to approach their congregations on these issues. The feedback from this workshop turned out to be very helpful in shaping effective science and faith seminars for this ongoing project. In fact, in retrospect, the entire ordeal resulted in several lessons that have either added to the success of this project or will contribute to the success of future projects.

First of all, I realize now that I should have involved college- and university-level administration from the very beginning of the project, in all aspects of the project, including the selection of team members. I also learned that unity can be maintained in the midst of diverse opinions if people are treated with care and respect, dialogue is preferred over debate, and emphasis is placed on what we all have in common, rather than focusing solely on areas of disagreement. If we can maintain these priorities, occasions of apparent conflict between science and faith may actually end up being opportunities to learn more about our Maker and his creation. In taking advantage of these opportunities, we will grow deeper in love with our Maker, and find ourselves better able to steward all that he provides for our enjoyment. The next chapter discusses further how concepts from the field of engineering can assist in this process.

STUDY QUESTIONS

1. Have you ever asked difficult questions regarding the Christian faith? How have people responded? What has been your experience in these situations?

2. How are worldviews like an ongoing jigsaw puzzle?

3. Why is an engineering mindset helpful when testing the accuracy of a worldview?

4. Place the six components of a worldview in order of importance. Why did you choose this particular order?

5. Place the nine tests of a worldview in order of importance. Why did you choose this particular order?

6. Keeping in mind the dangers of egocentric and socio-centric thinking, evaluate your own worldview using a scale of one to ten on each of the nine critical tests.

7. What does Pearcey argue regarding atheistic worldviews?

8. In what ways is science necessarily limited?

9. Why will any attempts to reverse-engineer the universe, including ourselves, have inherent limitations?

10. According to Rau, what strongly influences the conclusions we draw regarding origins?

11. With which of the six origins models do you most closely associate?

12. How does the Principle of Total Evidence apply to Origins research? What are its implications?

13. According to Rau, how will the greatest advances in origins research most likely come?

14. Describe a time in your life when you heard from God. What makes you think it was God speaking to you?

15. Describe a situation when you had to compromise to move forward. What important lessons did you learn from this process?

ENDNOTES

1. Biologos.org/about
2. Biologos.org/about
3. Kenneth Richard Samples, *A World of Difference: Putting Christian Truth-Claims to the Worldview Test* (Grand Rapids, MI: Baker, 2007), 23–28.
4. Samples, *World of Difference*, 33–37.
5. Samples, *World of Difference*, 37.
6. Richard Paul and Linda Elder, *Critical Thinking: Concepts and Tools* (Tomales, CA: Foundation for Critical Thinking, 2014), 21.
7. Paul and Elder, *Critical Thinking*, 22.
8. R. R. Reno, *Fighting the Noonday Devil and Other Essays Personal and Theological* (Grand Rapids, MI: Eerdmans, 2011), 92–101.
9. Samples, *World of Difference*, 267–75.
10. Samples, *World of Difference*, 275.
11. Nancy Pearcey, *Finding Truth: 5 Principles for Unmasking Atheism, Secularism, and other God Substitutes* (Colorado Springs: David C Cook, 2015), 177.
12. Pearcey, *Finding Truth*, 49.
13. Sam Harris, *The Moral Landscape: How Science Can Determine Human Values* (New York: Simon and Schuster, 2011).
14. Brian D. Earp, "Science Cannot Determine Human Values," *Think: A Journal of the Royal Institute of Philosophy*, 15, no. 43 (2016): 17–23.
15. Marcelo Gleiser, *The Island of Knowledge: The Limits of Science and the Search for Meaning* (New York: Basic, 2014), 282.
16. John A. Wheeler, *Scientific American* 267 (1992).
17. Gleiser, *Island of Knowledge*, 280–81.
18. John Jefferson Davis, *The Frontiers of Science and Faith: Examining Questions from the Big Bang to the End of the Universe* (Downers Grove, IL: InterVarsity, 2002), 92.
19. Nigel J. Cutland, "What does Gödel Tell Us?" *Science and Christian Belief* 3, no.1 (1991): 54.
20. Noson Yanofsky, *The Outer Limits of Reason: What Science, Mathematics, and Logic Cannot Tell Us* (Cambridge, MA: MIT Press, 2013), 24.
21. Gerald Rau, *Mapping the Origins Debate: Six Models of the Beginning of Everything* (Downers Grove, IL: InterVarsity, 2012), back cover. For a reformed perspective, see also Deborah B. Haarsma and Loren D. Haarsma, *Origins: Christian Perspectives on Creation, Evolution and Intelligent Design* (Grand Rapids, MI: Faith Alive Christian Resources, 2011).
22. Rau, *Mapping the Origins Debate*, 31–55.
23. Rau, *Mapping the Origins Debate*, 20.
24. Rau, *Mapping the Origins Debate*, 25–30.
25. Rau, *Mapping the Origins Debate*, 24–25.
26. Richard Swinburne, *The Existence of God* (New York: Oxford University Press, 2004).

27. Rau, *Mapping the Origins Debate*, 174.

28. *Old-Earth or Evolutionary Creation? Discussing Origins with Reasons to Believe and BioLogos*, edited by Kenneth Keathley, J. B. Stump, and Joe Aguirre (Downers Grove, IL: InterVarsity, 2017). These two groups have made significant progress toward Christian unity, even though they disagree on the issue of evolution with common descent.

29. Todd Charles Wood and Darrel R. Falk, *The Fool and the Heretic: How Two Scientists Moved beyond Labels to a Christian Dialogue on Creation and Evolution* (Grand Rapids, MI: Zondervan, 2019). Todd Wood is sometimes labeled a fool for his skepticism regarding mainstream scientific evidence on the age of the earth, while Darrel Falk is sometimes called a heretic for his belief that God worked through evolutionary processes over long periods of time, hence the provocative title.

30. "What's so funny 'bout peace, love and understanding" is a song made famous by Elvis Costello and the Attractions.

31. Reasons.org/about/our-mission

CHAPTER THREE

Engineering Brings Science and the Humanities Together

FINDING THE FUN IN PHYSICS AND ENGINEERING

"You're going to do WHAT?" shouted my mom when she heard of my older brothers' plan to try their hand at home-made parasailing. But they had already grabbed the keys to the station wagon, and were out the door with an old parachute in one hand and a glider tow rope in the other; their words trailing off in the distance, "Don't worry, Mom. It's not that dangerous." So began one of the most memorable days of my exuberant childhood. You see, I was blessed to grow up in a big family on a small airport among the fertile farmlands of north central Indiana; a very encouraging environment for a young explorer.

Evidence suggests that the universe began with a big bang, when all matter and energy, even space and time, plus an astounding amount of information content, sprang onto the scene from "who knows where." We know that the original state of the cosmos was loaded with information because the products of the ensuing expansion have evolved into very organized and orderly structures. Systems such as stars, galaxies, solar systems, and at least one rocky, water-soaked planet serve as excellent laboratories for the appropriate education of intelligent life. In reference to my older brothers, however, the word "intelligent" is used with some generosity (tongue-in-cheek). They had a lot of mass and energy, and plenty of space and time, at their disposal. What they lacked was the detailed information about how all these quantities interacted; hence their investigation into attaining high speeds and/or large forces in an effort to launch someone to great heights in the hopes of later returning him or her safely to the earth. I remember thinking at the time that the third and final phase of their research appeared to be somewhat of an afterthought.

On one unforgettable occasion, while Interstate 65 was being constructed about a mile from our home, my brothers discovered a couple of very large pits that had filled with rainwater. They had eventually developed a thick covering of ice during that particularly cold and windy winter. I recall hanging on for dear life as my brothers hitched a parachute to my flexible flyer sled, which quickly sent it shooting across the ice, like a hockey puck whose velocity only diminishes when it smacks into something really hard.

But to their credit, they did start small, carefully investigating various ways to harness the forces of nature in an effort to gain excessive speed and/or altitude. Actually, they were fairly innovative in combining assorted resources that could be found at a small airport with those typically found out on the farm. One early example of this was the time they tied one end of a glider tow rope to the top of our windmill. Since the tow rope was much longer than the windmill was high, several of my older siblings could grab hold of the other end of the rope and run away from the windmill at breakneck speed.

You're probably wondering why they would want to do that, other than to receive a big yank backwards when they run out of slack. Well, now imagine my brother David, also standing on the ground (initially), between the others and the base of the windmill, and holding tightly onto the rope at approximately its midpoint. That's right; if you know anything about geometry and forces, you know that David won't be standing on the ground for long. David is basically launched into the air, being plenty strong enough to keep hold of the rope as it flings upward, approaching tautness. A smooth ride is facilitated by "jumping into the launch" to soften the liftoff, sort of like when a pole-vaulter leaps into the air as the pole is planted in the box (see Figure 3–1).

Figure 3–1   An Early Version of a Homemade Launch Pad
Source: Dominic Halsmer

But alas, as with the pole-vaulter and every other flying object that has not attained escape velocity, what goes up must come down. Here's where the dynamics get interesting. Several factors influence the speed and orientation with which David returns to the ground. Did the group maintain some tension in the rope or did they just let go? (This latter procedure, though requiring precise timing and coordination, is considered to be bad form.) Did the upward force of the rope induce any swinging motion? Did David attempt any advanced maneuvers like an "over the rope" or front/back flip? After their initial success with this concept, they attached a loop of rope to serve as a kind of seat, to make it easier for the smaller children, like me, to have a ride. I have to admit that it was a very thrilling experience for a little boy.

Sometime later on a very windy day, the thought of using a parachute to catch the wind and gain altitude was imagined. This concept was tested behind our back woods in an open space to garner the full force of the wind. The parachute was tethered to a fence post and allowed to fill with the sweet summer breezes that rolled off the new corn and bean fields surrounding our property. On this particular day, the wind wasn't quite strong enough to keep any of my older brothers continuously airborne. But they enjoyed making huge leaps like they were astronauts on the surface of the moon, or basketball players with "flubber" on the bottom of their shoes.[1]

Of course they soon discerned that lighter people rose higher in the wind, and before I realized what was happening, they had grabbed me and were fastening the parachute harness around me. I didn't complain too loudly, as I was looking forward to bobbing up and down under the unseen power of the wind. I think it was then that I started to really appreciate the laws of physics because the combination of lift and gravity forces caused me to jump higher than any of my brothers (see Figure 3–2)!

Figure 3–2   Using a Wind-Filled Parachute for Ascension
Source: Dominic Halsmer

In fact, I was staying up for long periods of time, borne aloft by the wind, and the joyous cheers of success issuing from my brothers' smiling faces. They were acting like scientists or engineers who had just realized a major discovery that would positively impact humanity. I, on the other hand, was relishing the idea that I had excelled at something that even my older brothers couldn't do! It was a great day, but it was only the beginning of home-grown experiments which would assist in investigating the surprising utility of parachutes for *ascension*.

Engineering Makes Connections between Science and Human Values

In a previous chapter, I suggested that science cannot be used to determine human values. Although science has been very successful in helping us understand how the world works in-and-of-itself, it appears to be incapable of distinguishing good and evil, or establishing what we *ought* to do or how we should act. However, science certainly provides the "raw material" for engineers to use in bringing good things into people's lives. Based on knowledge of how the world works, engineers arrange things to accomplish purposes, solve problems, or improve the quality of life. They create relationships that result in the expansion of human capabilities and enjoyment. In other words, engineers create positive affordances that contribute to human flourishing. And they try to minimize the number of negative affordances that inadvertently arise in the process.

The preceding stories of my older brothers' rudimentary experiments with flight may seem like trivial examples in this regard, but the deeper significance of these events should not be overlooked. Of course, establishing the right relationship between a large piece of fabric and a human being affords levitation on a windy day. But that only scratches the surface of what was truly afforded. These activities afforded entertainment, excitement, comradery, and joy. These simple acts of adventurous play bolstered confidence in teamwork, leadership, communication, and engineering skills. And they afforded an enthusiasm for science and engineering that ultimately influenced my choice of careers and remains with me to this day. In a way, engineering forms a kind of bridge between science and the humanities by taking the stoic pronouncements of science and creating both tangible and intangible benefits for people. These benefits range from the economic and the social, to the aesthetic and the spiritual.

In this manner, engineers serve as practical interpreters of scientific discovery. They help to determine what meaning and impact scientific discoveries will have for human beings. And they facilitate and shape this impact. So it is not too far-fetched to imagine that an engineering mindset might bring valuable assistance to the project of hacking the cosmos. How do engineers implement their ideas and establish the proper relationships to achieve their objectives? It is largely accomplished through the development and use of models of reality, which will be discussed in the next section. Models prove useful for transforming theoretical ideas into practical applications in both science and religion.

A Model Is Worth a Thousand Words

The world is a very complex place. One of the biggest challenges for people in virtually every field of study is how to handle this complexity. Scientists and engineers want to understand how the world works so they can accurately predict what will happen when they attempt to manipulate things in the world. Consider the example of sending people to the moon and back. This ambitious project presented a tremendous technical challenge. Not only did engineers have to develop a rocket with enough punch to safely achieve escape velocity, but they also had to navigate the changing environmental conditions associated with a trip to the moon. This involved multiple vehicles and devices that could continue to function properly in the changing temperatures, pressures, and gravitational fields entailed by such a voyage. And all engineered with enough accuracy and precision to afford a high level of confidence that a safe return to the earth would be achieved. (See Figure 3–3)

Figure 3–3   Saturn V Moon Rocket in Flight on July 16, 1969
© Everett Historical/Shutterstock.com

What was the key to accomplishing this incredible feat? At the most fundamental level, the key was having enough knowledge of rocket science and our earth-moon system to allow the development of the necessary *models*. These models were then used to predict what would happen if certain forces, devices, and procedures were to be applied. In the technical sense then, models are simplified representations or pictures of reality that allow this reality to be simulated, better understood, and perhaps manipulated to achieve some purpose. A worldview is simply a comprehensive model of all that exists. In science and engineering, models are often mathematical since the language of mathematics has been found to be extremely (some would say unreasonably[2]) effective in describing the physical world. For example, mathematical formulas are used to predict the varying gravitational forces that pull on a spacecraft, depending on whether it is near the earth, midway between the earth and moon, or closer to the moon.

Engineers are known for their ability to develop helpful models, even though they may only be approximations to reality. Modeling is the art of simplifying a complex system in a way that still captures important aspects, allowing our purposes to be achieved. It's been said that, "You know you're an engineer if . . . you'll assume a horse is a sphere in order to make the math easier." This sounds like an absurd assumption, but it can actually be quite useful in making a quick calculation of how much heat is generated in a stable full of horses. It should be clear then that a model need not be a perfect representation of reality to be helpful. In fact, if it was perfectly accurate, it probably wouldn't be helpful at all because it would be too complex. Scientist E. P. Box put it succinctly when he wrote, "Essentially, all models are wrong, but some are useful."[3] This is an important feature of models that holds true even beyond the fields of science and engineering.

Some models are mathematical, or quantitative, in nature, but some models are more qualitative. This is true of the use of analogies in theology to help in understanding the concept of God. These kind of models have a lot in common with models used in science and engineering. In his book, *Science and Religion: A New Introduction*, Alister McGrath discusses these similarities. In neither area are these models literal depictions of reality. Models are approximate organizing images that allow us to structure and interpret events, ultimately relating to observational data (science and engineering) or personal experience (theology).

However, theological models differ from scientific models in that they serve non-cognitive functions, and evoke more total personal involvement. Indeed, theological models appear to be more influential than the formal beliefs and doctrines which are derived from them, while scientific models are subservient to the scientific theories to which they are related.[4] The model proposed in this book is a combination of theological and technological ideas. A model of God as refiner or process systems engineer is a biblical and theological construct based on scientific principles and engineering applications. This model will be explored further in the final section of this book.

Engineering Models in Systems Biology

In the last few years, engineering models have proven to be extremely useful in helping scientists understand how living systems work. In fact, the more that scientists and engineers learn about natural systems, the more similarities they uncover between human engineering and the way nature works. This is especially true for living systems. Biologist E. O. Wilson writes that "the surest way to grasp complexity in the brain, as in any other biological system, is to think of it as an engineering problem . . . Researchers in biomechanics have discovered time and again that organic structures evolved by natural selection conform to high levels of efficiency when judged by engineering criteria."[5] This seems to be the general consensus among current biologists; although there are differing opinions concerning the details of how these systems came to be, it is commonly agreed that they represent examples of exquisite engineering.

In his book, *Molecular and Cellular Signaling*, biologist Martin Beckerman asserts, "Biological systems are stunningly well engineered. Proof of this is all around us. It can be seen in the shear variety of life on Earth, all built pretty much from the same building blocks and according to the same assembly rules, but arranged in myriad different ways. It can be seen in the relatively modest sizes of the genomes of even the most complex organisms such as ourselves."[6] He goes on to describe how cellular organization and modularity (examples of "good engineering") facilitate the development and control of critical life processes.[7] In other words, the fundamental parts that make up living systems appear to be ingeniously arranged to afford life.

The January 2008 joint issue of the *IEEE Transactions on Automatic Control* and *IEEE Transactions on Circuits and Systems* was a special issue devoted entirely to "systems biology." The editors define systems biology as "the quantitative analysis of networks of dynamically interacting biological components, with the goal of reverse engineering these networks to understand how they robustly achieve biological function."[8] Similar approaches to understanding biology can be found in recent journals representing the biological and medical sciences.[9] If reverse engineering really is a fruitful way of studying natural systems, then this method of conducting science, which effectively marries the fields of engineering and science, should be thoroughly explored to ensure that maximum benefit is achieved. The implications of such an approach should also be investigated, which is one of the reasons for this book.

The process of reverse engineering has been used for many years but recently the application of reverse engineering in new areas has led to discoveries and better understanding of the functions and affordances of both natural and artificial systems. Knowledge of the bacterial flagellum (a natural propulsion system for bacteria), for example, is due largely to the application of reverse engineering techniques to biological systems.[10] Modeling and analyzing this biological structure as that of a motor sheds light on the affordances of the individual parts of the bacterial flagellum.

In another example, a biologist and an engineer teamed up to study the heat shock mechanism of e. coli bacteria,[11] using reverse engineering techniques such as "subtract and operate."[12] This entails removing part of the system to see the effects. They found that system performance degraded only slightly when feedback or feedforward information pathways were removed to simulate damage or corruption. They claimed that this robust system is remarkably similar to what a well-trained control systems engineer would devise. This idea of reverse engineering in the face of damage or corruption is an important consideration in dealing with natural systems,[13] as will be seen in the next section.

The "subtract and operate" technique can be effectively applied to analyze natural systems on a much larger scale as well. From a historical perspective, Nazi Germany of the twentieth century decided to subtract (eliminate) the Christian ideal of "loving one's neighbors." Not only did they stop caring for their Jewish neighbors in their own country, but on a larger scale, as a nation, they stopped caring for many of their neighboring countries in Europe, and around the world. The disastrous result of attempting to operate their plan of world domination in the absence of love was, in effect, a double Holocaust; the horrific decimation of the Jews in concentration camps, and the enormous loss of life associated with the years of intense combat during World War II. This attempt to form a new world order with a total disregard for neighborly love was a miserable failure, not only for Nazi Germany, but for the entire human race.[14] Hopefully, we have learned this lesson well. Love and care for neighbors, even those we may find difficult to love, appears to be a key aspect of human flourishing.

Objections to Engineering Models and Their Theological Implications

With the rise of the controversial Intelligent Design movement, some theologians and scientists have expressed concern that viewing God as an engineer is unhelpful and largely inaccurate; an unproductive throwback to the days of William Paley's Watchmaker Argument.[15] The esteemed John Polkinghorne even claimed recently that "God is never spoken of as a designer in the Bible."[16] Similarly, Catholic author Christoph Schonborn rebels against the idea of a "divine engineer" or "optimal technician," stressing instead that God is a creator of "natures."[17]

In response to these criticisms, it should be made clear that this motif of God as engineer is not an attempt to limit God to the category of human engineering, but rather to relate to God in a category in which he has clearly already revealed himself, both in nature and Scripture. In addition, if humans are made in God's image (Gen 1:26), they presumably would be blessed with some small fraction of his genius and creative problem-solving capabilities. Thus, it seems that God intends for human beings to relate to him in this manner, while simultaneously marveling at his awesome and mysterious transcendence.

Indeed, some theologians are quite comfortable with thinking of God in this kind of role, recognizing its significant scriptural support. Dennis Cheek writes, "God is sometimes presented in the Old Testament in a manner that we would today call a *systems engineer*. He creates (designs) a universe and world and places within it creatures, including human beings."[18] Other theologians recognize his role as "Creator-Craftsman,"[19] "arch-technophile,"[20] and "artisan."[21] Even so, this does not preclude the possibility that God engineers the laws of nature and leaves much of His creation to "deploy automatically," at least from humanity's perspective.

In this case, he would be considered more of an architect-engineer, rather than a builder-engineer. The proper balance in this regard (hence, the controversy over evolution) is one of the major questions that is still perplexing researchers at the interface of science and theology. However this question is ultimately answered, the Scripture is clear that "the Lord is fundamentally engaged in the design of patterns and the creation of systems. Yahweh engages in what we can only describe as technological activities combining human and nonhuman resources in various ways to accomplish his plans and purposes in the universe and principally among humankind."[22]

Of course, there are those who argue against such theological implications. Physicist and science writer Phillip Ball recently published an article in *Nature* entitled, "What a Shoddy Piece of Work is Man."[23] In this article he expounds on the idea that "the human body is certainly no masterpiece of intelligent planning." First of all, for someone to be "certain" of such a conclusion one would have to know much more about the origin and destiny of living systems than mankind currently possesses or is ever likely to possess. This kind of "overstating the case" occurs on both sides of the science and theology debate. It is unproductive, often leading to emotional responses, and should be avoided, and quickly corrected when recognized. Even so, it is understandable how Ball might come to his conclusion when one considers all the negative factors associated with not only the human body, but also the human condition.

Ball refers to the recent work of evolutionary biologist John Avise, who published a book entitled *Inside the Human Genome: A Case for Non-Intelligent Design*,[24] and a *PNAS* article entitled, "Footprints of Nonsentient Design Inside the Human Genome."[25] Avise makes his case by pointing out the deadly effects of malfunctioning aspects of the genome, seemingly wasteful elements, and baroque arrangements that no conscious engineer would conceivably produce, or even allow. Once again, it should be pointed out that in order to properly judge the merits of such a hypothesized design, one needs more complete information concerning the engineering objectives and other metaphysical factors that might bear on such a design.

Perhaps Ball and Avise might consider other possibilities such as the idea that natural systems have undergone some kind of corruption throughout their history, or even that a cosmic engineer allows negative factors to be introduced for the eventual good of his or her creatures. Instead, Avise closes his article by asserting that "Evolution by natural causes emancipates religion from the shackles of theodicy," since God is no longer responsible for the "gross evil and suffering in the world." A *Speed Bump* comic by Dave Coverly, published on 7/20/2011, and found at http://www.cartoonist group.com/store/add.php?iid=63489 accentuates the absurdity of this argument. It portrays an angel as God's spokesperson before a bank of microphones at a cosmic press conference. And claiming that just because God is CEO of the universe doesn't mean that he should be held responsible for every so-called "act of God."

Avise is corrected on this point in a reply to his article by Michael Murray (philosopher) and Jeffrey Schloss (biologist).[26] They point out that "positing that God delegated the task of generating life to insentient evolution merely ushers in an explanatory regress that serves to illuminate rather than ease the problem of the evils resulting from the operation of nature." In other words, if God is truly the Creator, then he is still ultimately responsible.

To Avise's credit, he appears to receive this correction, as made evident in his response to Murray and Schloss,[27] and is humble enough to invite non-scientists into the dialogue. In reference to "molecular faults that cause vast human suffering," he writes, "It is now time for theologians to *step up to the plate and perhaps help us to understand* the philosophical implications of this rather disturbing reality." This invitation and openness to cross-disciplinary dialogue is a welcome development that should be applauded by both sides of the debate. Engineers should also join the scientists and theologians at the plate since much of the discussion involves the reverse engineering of complex biological systems. This book is an attempt to do just that.

PARASAILING O'ER RUNWAYS OF GRASS

Although the parachute experiment (described at the beginning of this chapter) was considered a great success, it would have been an even greater success had my brothers been able to remain aloft. Thus, they set about the task of creating a bigger wind. This, they figured, was easily accomplished by attaching the parachute (via a long stretch of the glider tow rope) to the hitch on the back of our station wagon. This would be real parasailing, but the idea was as simple as flying a kite, and we all knew that the lift force on a kite could be increased by running with the kite. The perfect venue for this activity was just across the road from our house, but still on airport property, on a strip of land affectionately known as "The Grass Runway."

During all my growing up years, my dad and his two brothers owned and operated a small airport a few miles east of Lafayette, Indiana. By the time I was born, they had already installed a 4,000-foot hard surface runway, but had also kept the earlier, and shorter (approximately 1,500-foot), grass runway. Maybe they kept it as a reminder of their barnstorming days, when they would regularly take off and land in whatever grassy fields seemed to be large enough, and convenient for attracting the local townsfolk. Whatever the reason, my brothers deemed our grass runway, bordered on both sides by soybean fields, to be long enough, and otherwise appropriate for parasailing.

They probably figured it would work something like this: Someone would strap themselves into the parachute harness, and someone else would steadily pull them along with the station wagon as they bobbed gently to and fro a few feet above the surface of the grass runway. Notice how I conspicuously left out the part about taking off and landing. I'm not sure but I think maybe my brothers sort of left that part out too. It turned out that those were the key features upon which the success of this whole operation heavily depended. What actually happened was more like this: David strapped himself in and confidently gave the thumbs-up (all systems go) signal. The station wagon lurched forward in the deep grass, quickly consuming the slack in the tow rope, and yanking David off-balance as he attempted to run until the parachute filled, providing the all-important and much-hoped-for and please-oh-please-be-there lift force! As one might imagine, the station wagon continued to accelerate, since it's difficult to judge just how fast one is really going in a car, compared to how fast one is able to run.

Now David finds himself in a bit of a pickle, since an adequate lift force had not yet been generated. And although he ran track and cross country very successfully for Central Catholic High School, he didn't have much running experience when being pulled behind a station wagon. Thus he quickly found himself being dragged face-first through the grass. There was no "bobbing gently to and fro"; only sliding, and grass-stains, and "in-the-name-of-almighty-God-please-STOP!" Fortunately, they had enough foresight to have someone watching in the back of the station wagon who could quickly relay pertinent information to the driver, once they had quenched the temporarily incapacitating bout of uproarious laughter.

Undaunted by initial failure, a quick conference was held to see if a solution to this problem could be found. Within a few minutes, I found that I was being summoned, "Hey Dominic, we need your bike. Can you run and get it?" Now my only real prized possession in the world was my super-sport, single-speed, wheelie-popping, skid-the-back-wheel-in-the-dirt bicycle with a leopard-skin covered banana-seat and a sissy-bar on the back. It was my pride and my joy. Not realizing the unhealthy predicament my bike would soon find itself in, I responded with an enthusiastic "Sure!" and ran to get it. At that point, I was just happy to be able to contribute what little I had to the local aviation research effort. And I was very curious to see if my brothers really could fly once they got some help from little-old-me.

Actually, being able to ride the bike until enough lift was generated by sufficient speed made all the difference in the world. As David was lifted into the air, he cautiously held on to the handles of my bike until he was sure that the lift force would be sustained. Once he reached an altitude of ten or fifteen feet, he let go and I watched in horror as my bike suffered a spectacular crash to the ground with multiple bounces and flips. At the same time, I was filled with wonder and amazement that their crazy idea had been successful. David was flying high over the grass runway, his legs for the moment dangling uselessly in the air. Upon retrieving my bike, I was relieved to find that it was not too much the-worse-for-wear, although the handlebars seemed to be a little loose. I jumped on, straightened my handlebars, and sped after the chase group, who were running to see what kind of a landing David might be able to finagle (see Figure 3–4).

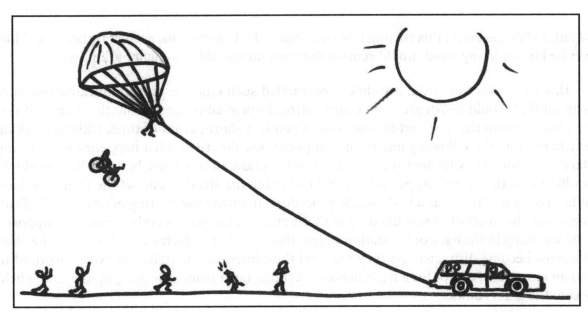

Figure 3–4   Parasailing behind the Station Wagon down the Grass Runway
Source: Dominic Halsmer

Now was the point in the flight when David wished he hadn't dropped my bike, but not because he was worried that he might have damaged it. The station wagon had run out of grass runway and was slowing down, which caused a slack in the rope, and a corresponding decrease in the lift force. As the ground quickly came up to meet him, David knew enough to windmill his legs in anticipation, running in the air like someone who . . . wished he had a bicycle. It is my recollection that his landing was very similar to his first attempted take-off; the one without the virtue of my bicycle. Imagine that! But the ignominiousness of that first landing would not dampen the joyous celebration of success that ensued as we rushed to congratulate him. It actually worked! They had done it! They had accomplished the miracle of flight without an airplane, using only an old parachute, a glider tow rope . . . and a station wagon.

Several of my older brothers "slipped the surly bounds of earth"[28] that day, with varying degrees of success and no serious injuries. Toward the end of the day, I remember David turning to the group and asking, in his kind and gentle voice, "Does anyone else want to give it a try?" There was a long silence, and I remember thinking, "no way," but then my brother Mark stepped out from the crowd. The look on his face was one of stark terror mixed with fierce determination.

Now I must have been about seven or eight years old at the time, and Mark, being three siblings my elder, with approximately two years in-between each, would have been about thirteen or fourteen years old. I'm sure that several people were thinking the same as me, "So young, and already willing to die." Actually, I admired Mark for his bravery and his willingness to risk minor injury in order to experience life to the fullest. However, the words Mark shouted as he gave the thumbs-up signal betrayed the doubts he harbored about his own longevity.

As he was pulled forward toward glory or oblivion, there was only a hint of regret in his voice as it trailed off in the distance, "If I don't come back, tell my girlfriend I love her!" We snickered as we ran after him. We all knew he was kidding, at least the part about having a girlfriend.

Decades after the event, this parting line from Mark the Courageous, as my brother would forever be known in my mind, would remain the most memorable moment of the day.

This wondrous time from my childhood carried such emotion and significance that later as an adult, I would construct a somewhat satirical poem commemorating the event.[29] It was the kind of poem that just sort of flows out of you in a short period of time, without working very hard at it. The following line from that poem best describes what happened next during Mark's attempt: "How he floated and flew, 'twas the grandest of scenes, but alas, he veered left, headfirst into the beans." Apparently David had made the steering part of the operation look quite easy. In reality, it was a fairly subtle procedure involving the shifting of one's weight from side to side in an effort to stay lined up with the runway. I don't remember who was supposed to be watching in the back of the station wagon this time, but unfortunately for Mark, they had somehow become distracted. As they renewed their intermittent vigil, they were surprised to find an empty sky, except for a fresh harvest of young bean plants shooting up out of the field next to the grass runway.

When the station wagon finally stopped and we were able to catch up to the spot where Mark had skidded to a stop, we were relieved to see movement and hear muffled noises among the bean plants. We rolled him over and he looked up at us and smiled, but we couldn't see any teeth! Fortunately they were still there, safe and sound in his mouth, but almost totally obscured by the large amount of dirt Mark had scooped up during his trip through the bean field. Again we were relieved to see his pearly whites come shining through as he did his best to spit out the dirt clods.

What happened next caused my opinion of my brother Mark to grow "three sizes that day."[30] As we helped him to his feet, he said that he wanted to try it again! His determination to make a successful flight, in the face of serious danger to his . . . face, and other body parts, made a huge impression on me. Maybe it was the barnstorming spirit of our dad coming out in his sons. We had all heard similar stories about Dad's first attempts to learn how to fly at the simple controls of his homemade aircraft. These stories and others were recorded by Josephine Halsmer (my mom) in a book on his life titled *Chosen to Fly*.[31]

As for my bike, much to my dismay, the repeated high-speed drops eventually broke the handlebars clean off by the end of the day. It was then that I realized, along with Mark, that advances in science and engineering do not come cheaply, but they can sure be a lot of fun. Even so, as we were heading back home across the road, I was crying tears of anger. David was attempting to ride my bike; struggling to steer it by grasping and twisting the end of the broken vertical shaft where the handlebars used to be. He added insult to injury by joking with me, saying, "Look Dominic. You can still ride it!" Of course, he knew that he could make it as good as new by simply welding the handlebars back on in our shop. This job was completed within a few days and I was tearing around the countryside on my bike once again.

I don't know if our guardian angels put in a lot of overtime while we were growing up, but it seems that somebody was watching out for us. I expect it was the same person who created such a wonderful playground for us here on planet Earth. I imagine the Creator was smiling down on our feeble attempts to understand the physical laws he put in place to govern the universe.

He probably chuckled at our creative experiments, knowing that our persistence would ultimately pay off. We would learn about His world in a way that simultaneously filled our hearts with joy; the joy of discovery, and the conviction that life is good, and good to share in loving harmony with others. It only makes sense that there is an ingenious and loving source for all this goodness.[32]

STUDY QUESTIONS

1. Describe a time when you conducted experiments to explore the laws of nature. This can be as simple as jumping out of a tree, or as complex as atom smashing in the Large Hadron Collider. What did you learn from these experiments?

2. In what sense does engineering form a bridge between the sciences and the humanities?

3. What early experiences contributed to your choice of major and subsequent career path?

4. What do scientists and engineers (and theologians) do to handle the complexity of their subject matter?

5. Describe an example of the "subtract and operate" technique in reverse engineering.

6. Discuss some scriptural passages that speak of God in the role of Designer or Engineer.

7. How might the concept of specimen corruption in reverse engineering help us understand some of the negative aspects of the human condition?

8. What was admirable about John Avise's response to Murray and Schloss?

9. Do you think sacrifice is an integral part of achieving success in science and engineering? In other aspects of life?

ENDNOTES

1. See *The Absent-Minded Professor*, a Walt Disney movie from 1961.

2. Eugene Wigner, "The Unreasonable Effectiveness of Mathematics in the Natural Sciences," *Communications on Pure and Applied Mathematics* 13 (1960): 1–14.

3. George E. P. Box and Norman R. Draper, *Empirical Model Building and Response Surfaces* (New York, Wiley, 1987), 424.

4. Alister McGrath, *Science and Religion: A New Introduction* (West Sussex, UK: Wiley-Blackwell, 2010), 107.

5. E. O. Wilson, *Consilience: The Unity of Knowledge* (Westminster, MD: Knopf Publishing Group, 1999), 112.

6. Martin Beckerman, *Molecular and Cellular Signaling* (New York: Springer, 2005), vii–viii.

7. Beckerman, *Molecular and Cellular Signaling*, viii.

8. *IEEE Transactions on Automatic Control* and *IEEE Transactions on Circuits and Systems* (January 2008): 4.

9. J. Himmelfarb, "Dialysis at a Crossroads: Reverse Engineering Renal Replacement Therapy," *Clinical Journal of the American Society of Nephrology* 1 (2006): 896–902.

10. P. Aldridge and K. T. Hughes, "Regulation of Flagellar Assembly," *Current Opinions in Microbiology* 5, no. 2 (2002): 160–65.

11. C. J. Tomlin and J. D. Axelrod, "Understanding Biology by Reverse Engineering the Control," *Proceedings of the National Academy of Sciences* 102 (2005): 4219–20.

12. Kevin Otto and Kristin Wood, *Product Design: Techniques in Reverse Engineering*, (Englewood Cliffs, NJ, Prentice-Hall, 2000), 204–06.

13. Dominic Halsmer, Ken Weed, and Sean McDonough, "Affordance-Based Reverse Engineering of Natural Systems with Possible Corruption," Christian Engineering Education Conference (CEEC), Trinity Western University, June 29–July 1, 2011.

14. Along similar lines, apologist Ravi Zacharias explores the unsettling consequences of removing God from human affairs in Ravi Zacharias, *Can Man Live without God* (Nashville, TN: Thomas Nelson, 1994).

15. William Paley, *Natural Theology* (Oxford, England: Oxford University Press, 2006), 7.

16. John Polkinghorne and Nicholas Beale, *Questions of Truth: Fifty-One Responses to Questions About God, Science, and Belief* (Louisville: Westminster John Knox, 2009), 57. For a counterexample, see Hebrews 3:4—"For every house is built by someone, but God is the builder of everything." The word translated "builder" in the NIV is from the Greek verb κατασκευαζω, which means "to make ready, prepare, build, or furnish"; very similar to the activity we know today as engineering. Thus, a reasonable rendering of the passage is, "For every house is engineered by someone, but God is the engineer of everything."

17. Christoph Schonborn, *Chance or Purpose? Creation, Evolution, and a Rational Faith* (San Francisco: Ignatius Press, 2007), 98.

18. Dennis William Cheek, "Is there Room for the Spirit in a World Dominated by Technology?: Pentecostals and the Technological World," in *Science and the Spirit: A Pentecostal Engagement with the Sciences*, ed. Amos Yong (Bloomington, IN: Indiana University, 2010), 194.

19. J. Newman, *Religion and Technology* (New York: Praeger Publishers, 1997), 117.

20. D. Alexander, "Worshipping God with Technology," *Cambridge Papers* 12, no. 4 (2003): 2.

21. M. Lodahl, *God of Nature and of Grace: Reading the World in a Wesleyan Way* (Nashville: Kingswood Books, 2003) 73.

22. Dennis William Cheek, "Theology and Technology," (PhD diss., University of Durham, 2007), 40–41.

23. Philip Ball, "What a Shoddy Piece of Work is Man," *Nature News Online*, May 3, 2010.

24. John C. Avise, *Inside the Human Genome: A Case for Non-Intelligent Design* (Oxford: Oxford University Press, 2010.)

25. John C. Avise, "Footprints of Non-Sentient Design Inside the Human Genome," *Proceedings of the National Academy of Sciences* 107 Supplement 2, (2010), 8969–76.

26. M. J. Murray and J. P. Schloss, "Evolution, Design, and Genomic Suboptimality: Does Science 'Save Theology'?" *Proceedings of the National Academy of Sciences*, 107:E121 (2010).

27. John C. Avise, "Reply to Murray and Schloss: Designer Genes?" *Proceedings of the National Academy of Sciences* 107:E121 (2010).

28. *High Flight*, a short poem written by John Gillespie Magee, Jr. Source: Library of Congress:

High Flight
Oh! I have slipped the surly bonds of Earth,
And danced the skies on laughter-silvered wings;
Sunward I've climbed, and joined the tumbling mirth
of sun-split clouds—and done a hundred things
You have not dreamed of—wheeled and soared and swung
High in the sunlit silence. Hov'ring there
I've chased the shouting wind along and flung
My eager craft through footless halls of air. . . .
Up, up the long, delirious, burning blue
I've topped the wind-swept heights with easy grace
Where never lark, or ever eagle, flew—
And, while with silent lifting mind I've trod
The high untrespassed sanctity of space,
Put out my hand, and touched the face of God.

29. *Low Flight*, a not-so-short poem written by Dominic Halsmer:

Low Flight
for Mark
I was young, . . . it was summer, . . . and school was OUT!
Of worries, my mind knew nothing about,
'cept whether to ride to the airport for candy,
then sit in the sunshine and watch the planes landing,
or whether to play in or outdoor war games,
or play football against Mark and Robert, . . . and James,
when excitement arose from an elder somewhere.
You could count on them to put fun in the air.
Naught did I know with his latest invention,
but that was exactly young David's intention!
He had fashioned a chute with a rope and harness
to be pulled by a car down the runway of grass,

but the trick of it all was to put up a person.
I can still hear them say, "Well, . . . who wants to go first, then?"
The gang was all there with a gleam in their eye,
to see if these fools really knew how to fly,
Lilly, Tim, Mark and Robert, and someone called "pickle."
Ken Knevel had come on his motor-bicycle!
One problem was this; they had too fast to run.
At the cost of my bike did they solve this one.
Soaring into the air, on my bike they would ride,
'til they reached a safe height, then they . . . tossed it aside!
Though my bike was never the same, could I care?,
for my brothers were flying like birds through the air!
Recall David's first ride? . . . Through the sky did he glide!,
taking care to steer clear of bean-fields on each side.
For the touchdown he got his legs going real fast,
then he promptly fell, sliding face-first in the grass.
But by far, the one thing I remember the most,
was the look on Mark's face as he stepped from the host,
and those words that he cried as he prepared to suffer,
"If I don't come back, tell my girlfriend I love her!"
He was kidding of course, as we watched him ascend,
For we all knew Mark never had a girlfriend.
How he floated and flew, 'twas the grandest of scenes,
but alas, he veered left, headfirst into the beans.
Now the driver in front's got to watch where he's going,
While the watcher in back keeps an eye on the towing.
With the watcher remiss in his duties somehow,
this made Mark's lower jaw sort of act as a plow.
When they finally stopped and we ran to his aid,
we were all struck with awe at the patch Mark had laid.
Why, he'd stripped a brand new grass runway bare!
parallel to the one that was already there.
When we reached him the sight was not pretty at all,
for Mark's mouth had acquired much dirt from the fall.
It appeared to us that his attempt had been foiled,
and I'm sure that we all thought his underwear soiled,
but the thing about Mark and that dirt-eatin' grin
was the fact that he wanted to do it again!
I learned something that day: to be willing to try;
to not be afraid; and to reach for the sky!
These concepts Mark helped me to comprehend.
I think much later on, . . . he did have a girlfriend.

30. From *How the Grinch Stole Christmas*, by Dr. Suess.

31. Josephine Halsmer, *Chosen to Fly: A 60-year Love Affair with Aviation—and Beyond* (Lafayette, IN: Apple Tree Press, 1992).

32. Mark Wynn, *God and Goodness: A Natural Theological Perspective* (London: Routledge, 1999).

PART II
Affordances and Their Providential Structures

CHAPTER FOUR

Affordances: Relationships That Provide Capabilities

TOYS AFFORD PLAY—A VITAL ASPECT OF HUMAN FLOURISHING

One of my earliest childhood memories is of digging through the two canoe-shaped toyboxes that lived under the fireplace hearth in our living room. As the eleventh of thirteen children, by the time I showed up it took a lot of digging to find just the right toy to suit my momentary fancy. Every Christmas Eve it seemed that our Christmas tree was practically buried under the pile of presents, many concealing shiny new toys for the younger children. We drew names from a hat, so you wouldn't have to obtain a gift for everyone in the family, which was judged to be overly burdensome. But the height of the present-pile was still very substantial.

For obvious reasons, Christmas was by far and away my favorite time of the year. When I was seven years old, my dad decided to take advantage of his perks as an airline pilot and surprise us all with a trip to the islands of Hawaii and Tahiti as our Christmas present for that year. We would all be in the middle of the balmy Pacific Ocean for the Christmas and New Year holidays. Although my older siblings jumped for joy at the announcement, my parents were surprised by my sudden crestfallen countenance. What?! No Christmas tree? No pile of presents? Since I was not yet mature enough to appreciate all the fun we would have on that trip, I sulked for several days. I think it was my brother Pete who finally extended mercy a few days before we left, and bought me a Hot Wheels racetrack set, complete with a loop-the-loop attachment. That was cool. But actually, I soon found that it didn't compare with building sandcastles on Waikiki Beach.

Indeed, when I think back to how I spent the majority of my childhood, it wasn't playing with items from a toy store; it was playing with nature's toys, digging in nature's toy box. I could often be found exploring in our back woods, or building forts, or climbing trees. I was not conscious of it at the time, but every tree on our property was assigned a climb-ability index in my mind. There were several large trees that scored extremely high, and visits to their tops rotated regularly into my daily activities.

We played football in one side yard, and high-jumped in the other. We played baseball, kickball, and disc golf in the front yard, and pole-vaulted and golfed in the horse pasture in the back. We played basketball on the driveway and raced our bikes all over the place. We played tag and "jump-or-dive"[1] in the pool in the summer and played hockey on it in the winter. One magical winter was immediately preceded by a very rainy fall. The flooded fields around our house were soon adequately frozen for any number of winter games involving large stretches of ice. And it seems like we tried them all. We even came up with some games of our own.[2] After a particularly heavy snowfall, we used snow shovels to make paths on the ice, eventually producing a large and intricate maze—the perfect venue for a game of freeze tag.

The universe, and specifically planet Earth, affords so many amazing things for human beings: life, shelter, nourishment, discovery, and play. Within the realm of nature we find an abundance of these happy affordances, "natural toys," with which to play: mountains to climb, oceans to sail, and skies in which to soar. I consider myself very blessed to have grown up in that time and place, and with a family that knew the value of play. Some researchers suggest that play is "the single most significant factor in determining our success and happiness"[3] as human beings.

Stuart Brown is a medical doctor who has founded the National Institute for Play. As the leading expert on play behavior in the United States, he writes, "Play is anything but trivial. It is a basic biological drive as integral to our health and functioning as sleep or nutrition. When we play, we are open to possibility and the sparks of new insight and thought. Play provides the glue for our relationships and fuels our creativity. In short, we are designed by nature to flourish and play . . . Whether it's through physical activity, social interaction, competition, adventure, or art, our need to play is hardwired into our brains."[4] As one who has never lost his love for play and maintains a deep appreciation for toys, both artificial and natural, I heartily endorse this perspective. I also thoroughly enjoyed a movie in which toys took center stage. A well-known character from that movie will help me further illustrate the concept of affordance.

"To infinity and beyond!" announces a resolute Buzz Lightyear action figure as he extends himself to his full length (almost a foot!), and prepares to fly off and save the galaxy from the evil Emperor Zurg in the hit movie *Toy Story* (1995). See Figure 4–1.

But in the immortal words of the Apollo 13 astronauts, "Houston, we have a problem." As Buzz has just learned from inadvertently viewing a television commercial about him, he is "not a flying toy." This special revelation comes as quite a shock to poor Buzz since he is convinced that he is a real Space Ranger, complete with terillium-carbonic alloy wings that rapidly deploy at the push of a button. Surely, such high-tech wings were engineered to provide him with the valuable affordance of flight. The special revelation he received must be mistaken (or badly misinterpreted). With these notions in mind, he gathers his courage and daringly launches himself from the railing at the top of the stairwell in a desperate attempt to fly!

Figure 4–1   Buzz Lightyear Suffers an Identity Crisis in *Toy Story*
© N Azlin Sha/Shutterstock.com

One of the endearing aspects of *Toy Story* is that the toys come alive (in the absence of humans) and express their thoughts and feelings. Actually, Buzz had good reason to think he was a real Space Ranger and not just a toy. On the surface, it looked like he had all the "right stuff." He had come to this realization through a simple reverse engineering process, in which he observed his various affordances and reasoned to the logical conclusion about his identity. He came in a spaceship, complete with a hyper-sleep chamber. He wore a space suit to afford protection in the vacuum of outer space. He kept hearing voices about "a secret mission . . . in uncharted space." He sported a wrist communicator to afford him regular interaction with his superiors at "Star Command." He could defend himself, if necessary, with a built-in laser and intimidating "karate-chop action!" And he had wings!

However, if he chose to look a little deeper, he might notice a few other things. His spaceship and hyper-sleep chamber were one-and-the-same cardboard box. The face-shield of his "space helmet" was obviously not airtight, even if it did do that "whoosh thing." And if his mission was so top secret, how come it was printed in big bold letters on the outside of his spaceship? His wrist communicator was a decal stuck to his arm right next to the raised plastic letters, "Made in Taiwan." Needless to say, he never heard a peep out of Star Command. According to his good friend Woody, his laser was actually just "a little light bulb that blinks." He couldn't even control his own "karate-chop action" (and it was largely ineffective anyway). And his wings were made of simple plastic that looked pretty cool when they deployed, but were not engineered to afford the kind of power and lift needed by this chubby and misguided little space man. We'll return to Buzz's plight near the end of this chapter.

Engineers Create Affordances by Arranging Relationships

Engineering involves the creative use of resources and ingenuity to accomplish a purpose or solve a problem.[5] This almost always involves the recognition and understanding of key relationships in nature. For example, early aeronautical engineers such as the Wright brothers recognized an important relationship between the wind and a bird's wing. Upon further study of this relationship, they realized that the slight curvature of a wing in the wind could produce a force large enough to lift a person. So they arranged for a set of wings to be pushed into the wind by an engine that drove two propellers while also arranging for the necessary flight controls, and the rest is history; the first airplane. Of course, they had many failures along the way. But drawing upon their creativity, knowledge, wisdom, and skill, they were able to arrange the right pieces into an ingenious machine, ultimately providing the affordance of flight. That's what engineers do. They arrange things to take advantage of key relationships in order to provide valuable affordances.

That's why engineering students are sometimes required to disassemble a complex device, such as a motor or power-tool, and analyze its "inner workings" in order to illuminate the ideas behind its design and operation.[6] They search for key relationships and identify connections within the device that result in the desired affordances. The technical name for this activity is "reverse engineering," and one who engages in it is called a "reverse engineer," or simply an investigator. If this analysis is conducted with a focus on affordances, then this activity is called affordance-based reverse engineering. This book explores the potential of applying affordance-based reverse engineering techniques to natural systems; indeed, the entire cosmos.

Engineering graduates may engage in reverse engineering activities in their careers since many industries conduct such projects as they seek to uncover competitors' secrets and use this information to improve their own products. Rarely does the reverse engineer have the luxury of interviewing the original designer of the device. That would make things much easier. But instead, the reverse engineer must often make careful measurements and subject the device to cleverly devised tests to extract the necessary information.[7] This is similar to the interrogation of a reluctant witness during a crime scene investigation. One must ask the right questions, and carefully interpret the responses, skillfully applying them to formulate the next round of inquiry until all secrets are revealed.[8]

Reverse engineering of human-made devices has a long history and many books have been written on the subject.[9] More recently, however, reverse engineering techniques have been successfully applied to natural systems. The new field of "systems biology" seeks to reverse engineer living systems, to better understand how they so deftly achieve biological function. Several researchers in this field have acknowledged that they make the most progress when biological systems are treated as if they have been engineered.[10] This is somewhat surprising, firstly, since there is no reason to even expect compatibility between the complexities of biological systems and the intellectual capacities of the researchers for understanding them,[11] and secondly, since there is no reason to expect that biological systems would lend themselves to standard engineering analyses. Furthermore, the capabilities and efficiencies exhibited in biological systems far exceed those of similar humanly engineered systems.[12]

Another rapidly growing field called biomimetics[13] testifies to the great value of the extraordinary engineering found in nature.[14] Returning to the idea of reverse engineering as interrogation, then what does nature appear to be telling us through this state of affairs? The first thing that comes to mind is a philosophical implication: The fact that natural systems are so readily and profitably reverse-engineered by human beings suggests that such systems were engineered in the first place.[15] The implications speak of intentionality, purpose, and exquisite engineering expertise undergirding the entire realm of nature.

Recent developments in the field of engineering are serving to refine the reverse engineering process in a way that may make it even more applicable in biology. Borrowing from the ecological movement in psychology, design engineer Jonathan Maier claims that the concept of "affordance" is the underlying and unifying principle in engineering design, and, hence, also in reverse engineering.[16] In engineering terms, an affordance is simply what an environment or object provides to an end user. Solid ground affords walking, chairs afford sitting and perhaps stacking for convenient storage, and smartphones afford a multitude of capabilities that were thought impossible only a few years ago. Maier's work will be discussed further in what follows, but first, let's consider a brief history of the concept of affordance, from its early days in psychology to its current use in engineering.

Affordances Get Their Start in Psychology

The usefulness of affordances was first proposed by advocates of Gestalt psychology in the early twentieth century. Kurt Koffka writes that affordances are directly perceived in nature, resulting in the idea that things "tell us what to do with them." He continues, "Each thing says what it is . . . . a fruit says 'Eat me'; water says 'Drink me'; thunder says 'Fear me'; and woman says 'Love me.'"[17] Not to diminish the romantic quality of Koffka's list, it seems appropriate in this context to offer a gender-neutral twenty-first-century update as, " . . . humanity says 'Love me.'" This recognition by Koffka represents the idea that humans were made to be loved, and suggests that our purpose, both individually, and as a species, must have something to do with our unique ability to love. Christian theology proposes that the fundamentally human affordance of love, redeemed and empowered through the expression of love inherent in the incarnation, life, death, and resurrection of Jesus Christ, is the primary means by which we are invited to enter into an eternal loving relationship with our Maker. According to Proverbs 19:22, "What a person desires is unfailing love."

Psychologist James Gibson brought this concept up-to-date in applying it to ecological psychology in the 1970s in his seminal work, "The Theory of Affordances."[18] He asserts that affordances can be positive or negative, and that they may sometimes be hidden from the senses. For example, water affords hydration, washing, and swimming, but it also affords drowning, as with an imperceptible undertow that sometimes occurs near the ocean shore. Gibson claimed that people directly perceive affordances in their environments. However, Gibson's wife, Eleanor, also an ecological psychologist, claimed that "learning about affordances entails exploratory activities."[19] She studied the things people, especially children, do in perceiving affordances and acquiring knowledge.

James Gibson also suggests that when animals engage in a certain way of living in an environment, they make use of a niche, which is simply a set of affordances. Psychologist Rob Withagen et al. argue that,

> the concept of affordance might also help to clarify the process of niche construction . . . what this process actually consists in at a behavioral level is the perception, utilization, destruction and creation of affordances. Indeed, in constructing a niche, animals perceive and uti-

lize affordances and by so doing create and destroy other action possibilities. Hence, an affordance-analysis cannot only help in clarifying how the niche is constructed, it also helps in understanding what the modification of a niche consists in. Indeed, animals bring about changes in the affordance layout and this modified layout is passed on to the offspring.[20]

In applying these ideas to human beings, it becomes clear that our behavior, and the daily choices we make, significantly impact not only the set of affordances available to ourselves, but also to our descendants. This concept has been repeatedly confirmed by studies in the emerging field of epigenetics, which explores how organisms change due to many factors, including their environment and lifestyle.

In another paper, Withagen et al. explore the relationship between affordances and agency and emphasize the idea that, "affordances are not mere action possibilities but that they can also invite behavior."[21] This is seen in the way that a door handle is often engineered to invite pulling, as opposed to pushing, providing a clue to the intended behavior. Is it possible that this universe full of affordances plays a key role in inviting us into a relationship with our Maker? According to Romans 1:20, the entire realm of nature provides something of an invitation by affording (limited) knowledge of God, through an understanding of what has been made. It is thought that the scientific concept of affordance, combined with techniques in reverse engineering, may provide a new and helpful way of understanding God's providence and interaction with the world.

Engineers Borrow a Useful Concept

Cognitive psychologist and computer scientist Donald Norman was the first to introduce affordances to the field of engineering. In his book, *The Design of Everyday Things* (revised and expanded edition), he writes that, "An affordance is a relationship between the properties of an object and the capabilities of the agent that determine just how the object could possibly be used . . . affordances provide strong clues to the operation of things."[22] His reference to "clues" here provides confirmation that the identification of affordances also proves helpful when conducting reverse engineering studies.

In the new edition of his book, he introduces the idea of a *signifier*. He writes, "Good design requires . . . good communication of the purpose, structure, and operation of the device to the people who use it. That is the role of the signifier." For Norman, the term signifier refers to any perceivable indicator that communicates appropriate behavior to a person.[23] For example, a windsock is a special type of cylindrical flag, typically installed at airports to indicate the wind direction and approximate intensity. This serves as a signifier since it provides a simple visual indicator of whether it might be too windy to safely fly a light aircraft. In natural systems such as human beings, a universal internal sense of right and wrong appears to serve as a natural signifier for how we should live our lives. More about this in a later chapter.

Researcher William Gaver writes, "Affordances should be useful in exploring the psychological claims inherent in artifacts and the rationale of designs."[24] He also explores the idea of hidden affordances further, introducing the concept of "sequential affordances . . . to refer to situations in which acting on a perceptible affordance leads to information indicating new [previously hidden] affordances." He continues, "Sequential affordances explain how affordances can be revealed over time;

nested affordances describe affordances that are grouped in space . . . The role of a good interface [between engineered system and user] is to guide attention via well-designed groups of sequential and nested affordances."[25] These interdependent affordances not only reflect good design, but also provide important clues for reverse engineering. Future chapters will explore how the universe contains both sequential and nested affordances that appear to be vital for sustaining human life and signifying important concepts for humans to consider.

In thinking specifically about the human perceiver, psychologist John Pickering takes this idea further, writing that, "The characteristic reflexivity of human cognition means that we are not only able to perceive the world as it is, . . . but also to perceive affordances that do not yet exist, that is, to perceive the world as if it were otherwise . . . and hence we may take meaningful, intentional action to bring it about if we so choose." He adds that, "nature is a harmonious sign system," and that affordances are signs that are indicative of meaning and purpose in the world. Thus, affordances appear to be critically important for studying "the interactions of animals, plants and their surroundings [which] are the concern of biosemiotics, the study of natural signs."[26]

In his book, *Natural Signs and Knowledge of God*, C. Stephen Evans explores the natural signs associated with the three primary theistic arguments (cosmological, teleological, and moral). He concludes that these signs afford a universally available knowledge of God, but in a way that also afford humans with the ability to resist this knowledge, if they so choose.[27] This is consistent with the aforementioned, necessarily non-compelling nature of an invitation into a loving relationship.

Advantages of Affordance-Based Reverse Engineering

Undoubtedly, Jonathan Maier is the engineering researcher who has most thoroughly explored the potential of the concept of affordance for assisting with engineering design and reverse engineering. He claims that affordance-based design is a "relational theory for design" since it helps to "explain the entanglement between designers, users, and [engineered] artifacts."[28] He also proposes "an affordance-based method for reverse engineering and redesign."[29] This involves the careful analysis of an existing system "to see how it works and could possibly be improved."[30] Could these ideas be applied to natural systems such as human beings? Perhaps this is not too unreasonable given the widely acknowledged negative aspects of the human condition (need for improvement), and the recent success of reverse engineering in systems biology.

Recall from an earlier discussion that engineers create affordances for their customers by recognizing and taking advantage of key relationships in nature. But nature already holds an abundance of affordances that provide for the possibility of human life. Consider the way the laws of nature, the fundamental forces of physics, and the other physical properties of our universe seem to conspire to produce vitally important chemical elements within the core of stars. Building blocks of life such as carbon, oxygen, nitrogen, and all the heavier elements are formed in such a way that they can combine into biomolecules that afford life processes. How is it that these sequential and nested affordances simply exist in nature? The prophet Isaiah asks a good question when he says, "Lift up your eyes and look to the heavens: Who created all these?" (Isaiah 40:26)

Living organisms are extremely complex systems. As such, they not only exhibit affordances (such as life) for the end user (such as humans), but also affordances between various parts of the system, which provides clues as to how living systems work. These part-to-part affordances[31] reveal the critical connections that must be made for life to persist. For example, the human heart affords the pumping of blood, while the lungs afford oxygenation of that blood to feed the tissues and muscles. And the brain affords simultaneous control over all these activities. Even at the molecular and cellular levels, a myriad of part-to-part affordances contribute to the "well-oiled" machinery of life.

Maier contends that after identifying and evaluating the affordances at every level, a system has been effectively reverse-engineered in the sense that its operation should be well understood.[32] This is possible because affordances exhibit *complementarity*. That is, they are relational in a way that illuminates how two things fit together to provide a capability.[33] A well-engineered set of stacking chairs affords reasonably comfortable and inexpensive seating (end-user affordance) to a crowd of people because the chairs are the right height and width for the average person. But they also afford stacking (part-to-part affordance) for convenient storage because they are engineered to easily fit together on top of each other. Typically, this is because they are light enough to lift, and "the seat is narrower than the legs, such that the legs of one chair can slip over the seat of another chair."[34]

Another advantage is that end-user affordances possess a kind of *polarity*, in that they can be positive (beneficial to the user) or negative (potentially harmful to the user). Automobiles provide convenient and speedy transportation, but they also produce air pollution. Engineers continually face these kinds of trade-offs in their work. In creating any system, a good engineer will seek to maximize the positive affordances of the system, while minimizing the negative affordances.[35] This is why both positive and negative affordances must be identified during the reverse engineering process. As affordances are identified, the reverse engineer begins to see back into the mind of the original engineer(s); their intentions, abilities, and perhaps constraints under which they labored.

A classic defense of theism in the face of evil and suffering admits that God is constrained to allow for the possibility of such adversity in order to create free-will beings with the worthy ability to love. The prophet Jeremiah alludes to this when he writes, "Therefore this is what the Lord Almighty says: 'See, I will refine and test them, for what else can I do because of the sin of my people?'" (Jeremiah 9:7) Indeed, a great engineer is able to take something that has gone wrong, and somehow turn it around, causing it to work for good. Perhaps God is using adversity to refine and purify his people, preparing them for an eternity with their Maker. In light of this possibility, reverse engineers should remember that they have only partial information about these complex systems. Maybe it is premature to label adversity, such as suffering, as a negative affordance. It could be that as more information is gained in the future, we will come to appreciate suffering as a positive affordance.

Maier also notes that a system can possess a *multiplicity* of affordances.[36] Good engineering is characterized by a simple and elegant system that provides many positive affordances. The humble water molecule offers an intriguing example. Two hydrogen atoms readily combine with a single oxygen atom to produce the most useful and life-giving substance known to humans. Author Alok Jha documents the remarkable properties of water, including its fascinating origin in *The Water Book: The Extraordinary Story of Our Most Ordinary Substance*.[37]

But just because a system offers a certain affordance doesn't necessarily imply that it provides that capability at a high level. Thus, affordances have a *quality*, which describes how well the system affords a specific use or behavior.[38] And its quality may depend on the context of a given situation. Both a Barcalounger and a briefcase (standing upright) afford sitting, and while the Barcalounger may be a lot more comfortable, the briefcase may be a lot more convenient when scarfing down a hurried business lunch in a crowded plaza.

Natural systems present a puzzle in this regard. Many complex natural systems reveal affordances with incredible quality and efficiency. The DNA molecule safely stores vast amounts of information in a tiny space, far more efficiently than our best computers. But other affordances of the human body seem to exhibit questionable quality, such as a spine that affords upright mobility, but with a proclivity for back pain. And while the female uterus affords a secure environment while a baby matures, must the birth canal really be so narrow? This dilemma about the quality of natural affordances will be discussed further in a future chapter.

Finally, affordances are *form-dependent*. That is, they depend on the physical form of the system. This is helpful because it allows engineers to analyze and compare the affordances of various product concepts, as well as of existing systems during reverse engineering.[39] This helps in making comparisons regarding the quality of the affordances. Maier summarizes the situation nicely when he writes, "affordance based design allows designers to think about the design problem and all its requirements and all its embodiments and all of their ramifications within one conceptual framework.[40] An entire chapter is devoted to the concept of affordance since it will be a recurring theme throughout the rest of the book. The brief examples in the next section should help to further solidify these ideas.

The Big Picture of Affordance-Based Reverse Engineering

Maier claims that a relational theory for design with a focus on affordances helps to capture important interactions within the system of: (1) original engineer, (2) engineered product, and (3) user of the product. This triad represents the "big picture" of design, and considering the relationships between all three entities is important for successful engineering design.[41] In conducting affordance-based *reverse engineering*, a fourth entity must also be included in the big picture: namely, the investigator (or reverse engineer).[42] Once again, it is important to consider the relationships between all four of these entities during reverse engineering projects.

As an example, consider the capture of the damaged United States RQ-170 drone aircraft by the Iranian government in December of 2011. The Iranian government claimed that they were going to reverse engineer the drone in order to build and mass-produce a superior version.[43] In this case, the original engineer is the Lockheed Martin Corporation, the engineered product is the RQ-170 unmanned aircraft, the user of the product is the United States Air Force (or CIA?), and the investigator is the group of scientists and engineers hired by the Iranian government to do the reverse engineering.

The clearest picture of the situation is certainly obtained by considering the interesting relationships between all four of these entities. This example will be analyzed in detail in a subsequent chapter, but consider the following affordance that was originally built into the aircraft. Lockheed Martin was careful to encrypt the software that was loaded into the aircraft computer system in the event that this technology would fall into unfriendly hands. This makes any attempt to reverse engineer the aircraft very difficult, and affords the user (US Air Force) a higher probability of maintaining secrecy with regard to its advanced technologies, thereby affording a higher probability of maintaining air superiority.

Now consider an example from nature. In keeping with theologian Alister McGrath's *Open Secret: A New Vision for Natural Theology*, a Christian worldview will be hypothesized in order to explore how well it fits with the evidence from the study of nature.[44] In this case, God is taken to be the original engineer of the entire realm of nature. The engineered system to be investigated is taken to be the physical mechanisms involved in the sustenance of life on this planet. This includes not only the molecular machinery within living cells, but the total environment that provides multiple affordances (through what has been called "fine-tuning") that supports ongoing life processes.

The user of this system is taken to be humanity, who clearly benefits from the physical mechanisms of life that result in consciousness and all the other attributes that human beings enjoy as a part of living. The investigator in this case is taken to be that portion of humanity that desires to know the deeper truths regarding the system of life of which they are a part: How does it work? Where did it come from? Why does it exist? What does it mean to flourish as a human being? As in the previous example, interesting relationships exist between all four entities in this "big picture" of reverse engineering. All of these relationships should be explored to see how this picture of reality accords with the evidence from science, and all other fields of knowledge.

Again this example will be covered extensively in another chapter, so without going into all the details, one similarity with the previous example is worth pointing out. If the engineers at Lockheed Martin were clever enough to implement appropriate measures (encryption) to safeguard its users' interests in the event that their technology were to fall into unfriendly hands, how much more would God implement appropriate measures to safeguard his users (humanity) in the event that his technology (the world) were to fall into enemy (Satan) hands? Indeed, Christian theology posits that just such a situation has occurred.

In rebelling against God, humanity has found itself in slavery to an enemy of God. But God, in his wisdom, had already provided the sacrifice of his own Son, to afford us a second chance to enjoy eternity with our Maker. This is made clear in Ephesians 1:4–5 which says, "For he chose us in him [Jesus] before the creation of the world to be holy and blameless in his sight. In love he predestined us for adoption to sonship [and daughtership] through Jesus Christ, in accordance with his pleasure and will." In addition, God is depicted as a spiritual problem-solver in II Samuel 14:14 which says, "Like water spilled on the ground, which cannot be recovered, so we must die. But that is not what God desires; rather, he devises ways so that a banished person does not remain estranged from him."

It is believed that affordance-based reverse engineering of natural systems provides a rich structure that is capable of capturing many of the important interactions that need to be addressed to facilitate progress at the interface of science and theology. With this approach, the witness of nature need not be forcefully interrogated, for she seems to readily offer truths from her storehouse of treasures that further establish the coherence and veracity of a Christian worldview. Indeed, the heavens declare the glory of God; the skies proclaim the work of his hands. Day after day they pour forth speech; night after night they reveal knowledge (Psalm 19:1–2). All that is needed is a humble spirit to facilitate the asking of the right questions, a willingness to follow the leading of the Holy Spirit, and attentiveness to listen carefully for the voice of God in nature.

A CASE OF MISTAKEN AFFORDANCES

As you probably guessed by now, Buzz Lightyear dropped like a bowling ball when he leapt from that railing. He landed hard on the steps at the bottom of the stairwell, and broke his arm clean off. That was a wake-up call, to say the least. He ultimately realized that he was just a toy, but he suffered the consequences for his misconceived worldview. Fortunately, he was not damaged beyond repair. I recount this story to illustrate the concept of affordances, and how engineers use their ingenuity and resourcefulness to create valuable affordances for their customers. In a nutshell, this is what engineers do, and they typically do it with great success. Buzz mistakenly assumed that his "impressive wingspan" provided the affordance of flight, but instead, he simply ended up "falling with style."

Something similar often happens when engineered products are used in a way that exceeds their specifications. This typically occurs when a product is employed in a manner contrary to its purpose, as envisioned by the original engineer. For example, when a long screwdriver is used as a pry-bar, it may quickly and catastrophically fail because it was not engineered to be used in that manner. That is not the purpose of a screwdriver. It was not engineered to afford large prying forces, as can be achieved with a heavier crowbar or tire-iron. It was engineered to afford the application of torque necessary for the fastening (or removing) of screws. As a result, the now broken screwdriver is not fit to afford either large prying forces, or the fastening of screws.

Perhaps something similar has happened with human beings. From the very first humans to the swelling billions of this current era, somehow we get the idea that life affords autonomy; that we can be an autonomous Space Ranger, independent of our Maker, who, as such, is really our owner; that we can fly on our own, and enjoy all the wonderful affordances and goodness of life, without that vital relationship with the Maker, who engineered all those affordances with us in mind. Indeed, if we were made to be in that relationship and we choose to reject it to pursue our own purposes, we shouldn't be surprised if we fall and get hurt. If life has its origin and culmination in Christ, and we reject God's redemptive plan, why should we expect to remain unscathed and retain the affordance of life?

When Buzz finally realized that he did not possess the affordance of flight, and that he was not a real Space Ranger, "just a stupid little insignificant toy," he suffered a period of severe depression.[45] That is, until his friend Woody helped him understand that there is something better than autonomy. Buzz realized that he belonged to someone who loved him dearly. It's interesting that Woody had some issues to deal with in his own life before he was successful in helping Buzz see the light. Woody's pride and selfishness kept getting in the way, but once he recognized and repented of his own self-righteousness, the truth became crystal clear to Buzz. And he (spoiler alert!) enthusiastically accepted reality.

I hope that you find these parallels to be illuminating. It should be clear from the above discussion that affordances are key considerations in product design and reverse engineering. They are also incredibly helpful for obtaining a more complete understanding of natural systems, especially with regard to our identity as humans, and our place in the universe. The next chapters begin to discuss the implications of the incredible affordances that exist at all levels of the natural realm.

STUDY QUESTIONS

1. Given the importance of "play" for human health and flourishing, how will you continue to pursue these kinds of activities, even as you pass into adulthood?

2. Describe how engineering is simply the creation of affordances.

3. Describe the difference between (forward) engineering and reverse engineering.

4. Why is the success of reverse engineering in biology somewhat surprising?

5. What does the growing field of biomimetics and the successful application of reverse engineering to living systems imply?

6. Do you agree that love is the most important of all human affordances? What are some other vitally important affordances that humans possess?

7. What do affordances have to do with niche construction and offspring inheritance?

8. Meditate on Chapter one of Romans and describe how the physical universe affords knowledge of God.

9. What is the role of a signifier in an engineered system? Describe examples of signifiers from both artificial and natural systems.

10. How does the organization of multiple affordances in space and time provide important clues about origins?

11. Distinguish part-to-part affordances from end-user affordances.

12. How do affordances help a reverse engineer see back into the mind of the original engineer?

13. How might adversity be seen in a positive light?

14. In what sense do the quality and efficiency of natural affordances present a puzzle?

15. What are the six important relationships within the big picture of reverse engineering?

16. How does the big picture of reverse engineering assist in evaluating the veracity of a theistic worldview? How might it assist in evaluating the veracity of a Christian worldview?

17. How is the human condition illuminated by the image of an engineered product being used contrary to its purpose?

ENDNOTES

1. This sadistic activity involved lining up to run off the end of the diving board while a (usually older) sibling called out "jump" or "dive" at the last second. The victim was expected to promptly comply. The activity was generally considered successful and worthwhile if the timing of the call induced confusion sufficient to produce a horizontal entry into the water, otherwise known as a belly-smacker.

2. One of my favorites is "army man ping-pong," in which the same number of army men are initially placed on each side of the table, and each player tries to win by being the first to knock down all the other player's men by hitting them with the ping-pong ball. However, a man may not be knocked down on the serve.

3. Stuart Brown, *Play: How it Shapes the Brain, Opens the Imagination, and Invigorates the Soul* (New York, Penguin, 2010), back cover.

4. Brown, *Play,* front flap.

5. For a multitude of similar definitions for engineering see Raymond Landis, *Studying Engineering: A Roadmap to a Rewarding Career* (Los Angeles: Discovery Press, 2013), 278–79.

6. For examples see Corinna Wu, "Some Disassembly Required," *Prism* (October 2008): 56–59. See also Domnic Halsmer, Jessica Fitzgerald, P. Wesley Odom, and Taylor Tryon, "Implementation and Assessment of a Curricular Module on the History and Philosophy of Reverse Engineering in Biological Systems," Annual Conference of the American Society for Engineering Education (June 24–26, 2013), Atlanta, GA.

7. An example of this is the "subtract and operate" test, in which a part of the system is removed and the resulting degradation observed during subsequent operation. This and other techniques are described in Kevin Otto and Kristin Wood, *Product Design: Tecĥiques in Reverse Engineering and New Product Development* (Upper Saddle River, NJ: Prentice Hall, 2001), 204.

8. A marvelous example is provided by Detective Del Spooner (played by Will Smith) in the popular movie *I, Robot,* 20th Century Fox, 2004.

9. For a recent example see R. W. Messler Jr., *Reverse Engineering: Mechanisms, Structures, Systems and Materials* (New York: McGraw-Hill, 2014).

10. R. Eisenberg, "Look at Biological Systems through an Engineer's Eyes," *Nature* 447 (May 24, 2007), 376.

11. Such compatibility between specimen and investigator is a necessary prerequisite for the success of any reverse engineering project. Albert Einstein referred to this unlikely compatibility with this now famous quote, "The most incomprehensible thing about the world is that it is comprehensible."

12. Biologist E. O. Wilson writes, "The surest way to grasp complexity in the brain, as in any other biological system, is to think of it as an engineering problem . . . researchers in biomechanics have discovered time and again that organic structures evolved by natural selection conform to high levels of efficiency when judged by engineering criteria." See E. O. Wilson, *Consilience: The Unity of Knowledge* (Westminster, MD: Knopf Publishing Group, 1999), 112.

13. Biomimetics is the study of human attempts to imitate natural systems. See E. Jabbari et al., *Handbook of Biomimetics and Bioinspiration* (Singapore: World Scientific, 2014).

14. Biologist Martin Beckerman writes, "Biological systems are stunningly well engineered. Proof of this is all around us. It can be seen by the sheer variety of life on Earth, all built pretty much from the same building blocks and according to the same assembly rules, but arranged in myriad different ways. It can be seen in the relatively modest sizes of the genomes of even the most complex organisms, such as ourselves . . . The good engineering of biological systems is exemplified by the . . . partition of cellular processes into the fixed infrastructure and the control layer. This makes possible machinery that always works the same way in any cell at any time, and whose interactions can be exactly known, while allowing for the machinery's regulation by the variable control layer at well-defined control points. Another example of good engineering design is that of modularity of design. Proteins, especially signaling proteins, are modular in design and their components can be transferred, arranged, and rearranged to make many different proteins." See Martin Beckerman, *Molecular and Cellular Signaling* (New York, Springer, 2005), vii–viii.

15. This formulation of the argument from reverse engineering was first proposed in Dominic Halsmer, Nicholas Halsmer, Robert Johnson, and James Wanjiku, "The Applicability of Engineering Design Principles in the Formulation of a Coherent Cosmology and Worldview," Annual Conference of the American Society for Engineering Education (June 22–25, 2008), Pittsburgh, PA.

16. Jonathan R. A. Maier and Georges M. Fadel, "Affordance: The Fundamental Concept in Engineering Design," Proceedings of the ASME Design Theory and Methodology Conference (2001), Pittsburgh, PA, Paper no. DETC2001/DTM-21700. See also J. R. A. Maier, "Rethinking Design Theory," *Mechanical Engineering* (September, 2008), 34–37.

17. Kurt Koffka, *Principles of Gestalt Psychology* (New York: Harcourt, Brace and World, 1935), 7, 353.

18. James Gibson, "The Theory of Affordances," in *Perceiving, Acting, and Knowing*, ed. by R. E. Shaw and J. Bransford (Hillsdale, NJ, Erlbaum Associates, 1977), 67–82.

19. Eleanor J. Gibson, "Exploratory Behavior in the Development of Perceiving, Acting, and the Acquiring of Knowledge," *Annual Review of Psychology* 39, no. 1 (1988): 5.

20. R. Withagen and M. van Wermeskerken, "The Role of Affordances in the Evolutionary Process Reconsidered: A Niche Construction Perspective," *Theory and Psychology* 20, 4 (2010), 489–510.

21. R. Withagen, H. de Poel, D. Araujo, and G. Pepping, "Affordances Can Invite Behavior: Reconsidering the Relationship between Affordances and Agency," *New Ideas in Psychology, 20* (2012), 250–58.

22. Don Norman, *The Design of Everyday Things,* revised and expanded edition (New York: Basic Books, 2013), 11, 13.

23. Norman, *Design of Everyday Things,* 14.

24. W. W. Gaver, "Technology Affordances," CHI '91 Proceedings of the SIGCHI Conference on Human Factors in Computing Systems (1991), 83.

25. Gaver, "Technology Affordances," 82.

26. Pickering, "Affordances Are Signs," *tripleC* 5, 2 (2007), 64–74.

27. C. S. Evans, *Natural Signs and Knowledge of God: A New Look at Theistic Arguments* (Oxford: Oxford University Press, 2010), 191.

28. Jonathan R. A. Maier and Georges M. Fadel, "Affordance Based Design: A Relational Theory of Design," *Research in Engineering Design* 20, no. 1 (2009): 13.

29. Jonathan R. A. Maier and Georges M. Fadel, "Affordance Based Design Methods for Innovative Design, Redesign and *Reverse Engineering*," *Research in Engineering Design* 20, no. 4 (2009): 225.

30. Maier and Fadel, "Affordance Based Design Methods," 234.

31. Some researchers prefer to use the term "affordance" only in reference to end-user capabilities, and hence, object to the idea of "part-to-part affordances." Even so, these part-to-part "dependencies" (to use an alternate term) appear to play a key role in delivering the ultimate end-user affordances.

32. Maier and Fadel, "Affordance Based Design Methods," 235.

33. Maier and Fadel, "Affordance Based Design," 21.

34. Maier and Fadel, "Affordance Based Design," 25.

35. Maier and Fadel, "Affordance Based Design," 21.

36. Maier and Fadel, "Affordance Based Design," 21.

37. Alok Jha, *The Water Book: The Extraordinary Story of Our Most Ordinary Substance* (London: Headline Publishing Group, 2015).

38. Maier and Fadel, "Affordance Based Design," 21.

39. Jonathan R. A. Maier, "Rethinking Design Theory," *Mechanical Engineering* (ASME, September 2008): 36.

40. Maier and Fadel, "Affordance Based Design," 25.

41. Jonathan Maier, *Affordance Based Design: Theoretical Foundations and Practical Applications* (Saarbrucken, Germany: VDM Verlag, 2011): 41–61.

42. This quartet was first proposed in Dominic Halsmer, Nate Roman, and Tyler Todd, "Integrating the Concept of Affordance into Function-based Reverse-engineering with Application to Complex Natural Systems," Annual Conference of the American Society for Engineering Education (June 14–17, 2009), Austin, TX.

43. D. McElroy, "Iran to 'Reverse Engineer' US Drone," *The Telegraph* (Dec. 12, 2011).

44. Alister E. McGrath, *The Open Secret: A New Vision for Natural Theology* (Malden, MA: Blackwell, 2008).

45. "Years of academy training, wasted!"

CHAPTER FIVE

Affordances at the Microscopic, Macroscopic, and Telescopic Levels

A VISIT TO THE LOST WORLD

Douglas Adams wrote, "Time is an illusion. Lunchtime, doubly so."[1] Unfortunately, my mom never read *The Hitchhiker's Guide to the Galaxy*. One of my mom's favorite sayings before meal-time was, "Don't spoil your dinner!" She made it seem like we had the power to ruin the nutritional value of the meal she was preparing by indulging in some untimely snack. Of course, now that I think about it, a brown sugar sandwich (with plenty of butter to cement it together) right before supper could go a long way toward eliminating an appetite for vegetables. Often she would shoo us out of the house with, "Go and play. I'll call you when dinner is ready." This was easier said than done since we roamed far-a-field on, and even beyond, the five acres where we grew up. Fortunately, my Dad had installed a large dinner bell just outside our back door, attached to a swivel at the top of a tall pole with a long rope hanging down. By pulling on the rope, Mom could ring out the message that was so dear to our hearts during childhood. Like Pavlov's dog, the peal of that bell would immediately cause us to salivate, and we would most certainly drop everything and come running!

However, I have to confess that between the time we were shooed out the door and the time the dinner bell rang, I was often very successful at scrounging up something to stave off my hunger, at least for a few minutes. Obviously this depended on the time of year since snow and ice are not very filling or satisfying. But in the spring in Indiana, all kinds of good things become available for a child's dining pleasure. One of my favorite places to check was the rhubarb patch near the old horse barn. A fresh stalk of mature rhubarb was so sweet and tangy that it was next to impossible to eat straight away. A thin young stalk would last a long time by slowly sucking its juice out the end. When the juice was nearly gone, the fibrous stalk provided a nice chew; almost the consistency of bubble gum.

Next to the rhubarb patch was a grapevine that grew on an old white wooden fence. We actually had two grapevines in the yard, the other one climbing up the side of the pool house under the windmill. I remember climbing up onto the pool house in order to reach the riper, sweeter, dark purple grapes. The apple tree was an old standby, next to the garden, though the small yellow/green apples were rarely very good. Across the garden was a peach tree that often supplied good-sized peaches. One year, the tree was so laden with huge juicy peaches that a main branch broke under the weight and it never really recovered. The garden itself was often a fruitful place to check for something edible. However, my tastes had not matured enough to appreciate a nice ripe tomato or a fresh stalk of asparagus or broccoli. A carrot would have been good but we rarely grew them in our garden. Instead, we had learned how to spot the wild carrots that seemed to grow plentifully throughout our acreage. The shape of its leaves gave it away, and after it was extracted from the soil, that distinct carrot-smell confirmed that we had struck snacking-pay-dirt. No need to wash it off. We reasoned that the dirt provided extra vitamins and minerals for a healthy diet.

If one had an appetite for nuts, we had several large shagbark hickory trees and a couple black walnuts in the yard. However, extracting the nut meats took a little more work, especially the black walnuts which had a green outer cover over a black greasy substance which covered the hard inner shell which contained the meat. It was easier to expose the meat of the smaller hickory nuts by simply pulling off the four quadrants of the soft outer cover and tapping on the inner shell with a hammer. Still, the amount of meat per nut was minuscule, and there was always the possibility that a pignut had gotten mixed into the bunch. This was bad news for the taste buds, and to be avoided at all costs. Often it was more to my enjoyment to leave the outer cover on and test the accuracy of my throwing arm. The hickory nuts were plentiful and they were just the right weight and size for my little hands. Across the road was a huge, old, two-story barn with a metal window at the top which had fallen open a few inches. I could just barely reach it with a throw from our front yard, and every once in a while I would score by sending a hickory nut through the crack.

Along the fence rows that lined our property on the north and south, one could often find mulberries, blackberries, and black raspberries. The black raspberries were especially prized because they popped off clean without any stem to dilute the delicious berry flavor. There were a couple of bushes on the north side near the front driveway which usually produced, but never very heavily. It occurred to me one day, when I had a little extra time, to roam somewhat farther afield in search of berries. I knew that they liked fence rows so I explored across the road along an east-west running fence about a quarter of a mile from our property. This particular fence row served as the northern border of the small airport which my dad owned and operated with his two brothers. The land was mostly used for farming (corn, wheat, or soybeans), but a small percentage of it had been meticulously cleared of rocks to serve as runways and taxiways for airplanes.

This same fence row was significant for another reason. About a quarter of a mile from the road, it intersected a clump of about thirty large trees with assorted undergrowth known affectionately as "The Lost World." Later I would discover the origin of this spot to be the place where they dumped all the fieldstones when the airport land was cleared. But at that age, all I knew about The Lost World was what I heard from my ten older siblings. And they did a good job of promoting an image which lived up to its mysterious sounding name. I remember having a certain reverence or fear of the place, and it played on my nerves as I walked down the fence row toward it. It loomed larger now than I had remembered it. It always seemed so small when I inevitably glanced over at it from afar, while riding by in the car. Although I had visited it once or twice before, it occurred to me as I approached the outer trees that this was my first time to come here alone.

There was something strangely stimulating about being away from everyone and everything, and tucked within this oasis of foliage in the midst of the acres of farmland. I noticed that The Lost World had a distinct sound associated with it. In walking along the fence row away from our yard and that of our neighbors, it had gotten very quiet. But now the wind made an eerie sound as it blew through the branches of the trees. I half expected to turn around and meet a ferocious beast or a space alien, but as I explored its near side, I found only a sea of large stones and an old airplane wreck among the trees and bushes. I investigated the wreck for a while, climbing on the rusted steel tubing like a jungle gym and then moved on. I had practically forgotten why I came that way, when suddenly on the far side of The Lost World, I discovered something so wonderful that it immediately took my breath away. But first, let's consider the abundance of natural and nested affordances that humanity enjoys.

Engineers Help Open the Doors to Inner and Outer Space

For long ages, humans were constrained to exploring the world with their unaided five senses, with eyesight being the primary workhorse. But gradually, scientists, engineers, and technologists worked together to develop ingenious devices to enhance our exploratory capabilities. Engineers specialize in the study of how forces affect the motion of objects. A force is simply a push or a pull. Our ability to produce and measure forces on both large and small scales has significantly enhanced our sense of touch. The invention of explosives, like dynamite, allows us to produce large forces that are useful for exploring the interior of the earth. Seismometers are also helpful for understanding the nature of our planet since they are used to accurately measure the motion produced by earthquakes and volcanic eruptions.

But the two devices that have most greatly enhanced our sense of sight are undoubtedly the microscope and the telescope. Since they were both dependent on the development of precision optics such as lenses, they were both invented around 1600 CE. But advancements of the last one hundred years or so have dramatically increased their capabilities. In effect, these incredible inventions have ushered us into the heretofore undiscovered worlds of inner and outer space. And both of them have had a powerful impact on our understanding of human origins. Both the microscope and the telescope expand our vision into the dimensions of space, allowing us to tunnel into the extremely miniscule, and zoom in on that which is far, far away. But because of the dynamic nature of light, the telescope also allows us to effectively look back in time.

Since before the Common Era, debates raged about whether light had an infinite speed or just traveled really, really fast. The difficulty in measuring the speed of light was mainly due to our inability to precisely measure time. But in 1676, Danish mathematician Olaus Romer was able to overcome this difficulty by using a telescope to observe light being reflected off objects that were very far away. How far? Almost a billion kilometers! He noticed that the eclipses of Jupiter's moons did not occur at the times predicted by Newton's Laws. They are about eleven minutes too early when Jupiter and Earth are at their closest, and eleven minutes too late when they are the farthest apart. Romer correctly concluded that the discrepancy occurs because light takes longer to travel the larger distance. On this basis, he was the first to come up with a pretty good estimate for the speed of light, which we now know is about 300 million meters per second.[2] This is a good example of how the universe seems to be engineered to afford the discovery of its finer details by a curious humanity. Light, in particular, is not only key to these discoveries, but critical for life itself.[3]

Measuring the finite speed of light was a stunning advancement because it meant that if the speed of light has been constant over the history of the universe, telescopes could now be used to see into the past. This is simply because when we look at an everyday object, we are always seeing it as it was a fraction of a second earlier. It takes time for the light to travel from the object to our eyes. We don't often think about this effect because we're almost always looking at objects that aren't very far away, and light is really, really fast. But when we look at the stars, things are quite different. The nearest star (our sun) is so far away that it takes light about eight minutes to travel from its surface to our eyes. So when we see the sun, we're actually seeing it as it was eight minutes earlier. It's like looking eight minutes back in time, at least as far as the sun is concerned.

As telescopes have continued to improve, so has our ability to see more distant objects, and hence our ability to see even further back in time. As you might imagine, this has greatly increased our knowledge of astronomy (the study of celestial objects) and cosmology (the study of the origin and development of the universe). What we see is a dynamic universe; one that is evolving, or changing over time. Early in the twentieth century, the theoretical work of physicists such as Albert Einstein, and the observations of astronomers such as Edwin Hubble, fit together to provide a picture of an expanding universe. This was somewhat of a shock at the time since the force of gravity should tend to pull everything together. But what was even more shocking was the evidence of a beginning for the universe, when matter, energy, space, and time had some kind of a starting point, in what has now come to be known as the Big Bang. No one has a good explanation yet for why space is expanding, but at least we have a name for it: dark energy.[4]

During this same period, engineers were also helping biologists to see deeper into living systems by developing more powerful microscopes. They gradually came to realize that everything in the universe is made out of the same stuff: fundamental chemical elements (atoms) and sub-atomic particles that stick together in predictable ways to form molecules that serve as basic structures for both living and non-living systems. The twentieth century also saw the development of a theory that explained the origin of these elements through processes known as stellar evolution and nucleosynthesis. Observations confirm that stars change over time. As they progress through various stages and generations of burning, starting with hydrogen, they produce in their cores the heavier chemical elements of our periodic table. Atoms of carbon, oxygen, nitrogen, and iron, which are so vital for life, along with all the other chemical elements, are manufactured inside stars.

These elements are like natural Legos because they come together and attach to each other to form new molecules that are necessary for life. Then during vital chemical reactions, they break these bonds and form new connections with other molecules, delivering useful energy in the process. The key molecule for life appears to be deoxyribonucleic acid, or DNA, which is stored in every living cell, and makes up the human genome. In studying genomic data, biologists gain clues to the history of living systems. They explore how genomes have changed over time and draw conclusions about how life has adapted and developed. With the help of the microscope and other instruments, biologists have come a long way in understanding life processes at the atomic level, and they continue to learn more every day.

Isn't it fascinating that the secrets of inner and outer space have turned out to be connected in such fundamental ways? And that these mysteries were unraveled at about the same time to provide a coherent picture of the history of the universe and of life? Of course, we still have a lot to learn, and science is limited in what it can tell us, but the beginnings of various types of matter, and how it assembles to facilitate life processes contributes significantly to our understanding of human origins. Engineers play an important role in these discoveries by developing instruments that afford the extension of human vision. In doing so, engineers and scientists must work closely together to communicate requirements and operating procedures. Engineers create affordances for scientists. But they also recognize affordances in nature, and ponder the repercussions of those affordances. Let's begin to take a closer look at natural affordances and consider the implications.

Natural Affordances as an Objective Starting Point

Before proceeding further with a detailed discussion of affordances in nature, let me be clear about the inherent objectivity of this approach. An objective approach to understanding reality is not influenced by personal feelings, interpretations, or prejudice; it is unbiased, and based on facts.[5] Although this is a worthy goal, it is now widely recognized within the academic community that such an approach is virtually impossible. Human beings have a very difficult time being totally objective. Furthermore, data must necessarily be interpreted if meaning is to be assigned in a useful way. Thus, recognizing this difficulty is the first step in attempting an approach that is as objective as possible. Nevertheless, I will try to describe how I have arrived at my current perspective, as best as a human being can objectively analyze such things.

As is evident from previous chapters, I am a Christian. As such, I candidly admit that I approach the data of science and the humanities from a Christian perspective; I can do no other as long as I continue to hold this worldview. But I still have the ability to put myself in other people's shoes, to a certain degree. And I am attempting to be as objective as possible in handling the pertinent evidence. It's not as hard for me as you might think, even though I am a committed Christian. I don't think I have a deep emotional need for Christianity to be true. There was a time when I was not a Christian, and it's possible that at some time in the future I may renounce my Christianity. It's possible that the whole Christian thing is just all in my head.[6] But I don't think that I became a Christian because I wanted it to be true, or because it made me feel good. I concluded that the Christian version of theism is true based on the balance of accumulated evidence from all areas of human thought and experience that I had reviewed. Although I cannot detach myself from this worldview while I still hold it, I seek to present the evidence from nature in a fair-handed manner, and current research suggests that affordances provide the most objective place to start.

In the article, "Affordances: An Ecological Approach to First Philosophy," philosopher John Sanders argues that affordances "offer a conceptual tool of exceptional value in the construction of a positive theory of embodied agency [i.e., humanity], and of its philosophical consequences."[7] He claims that affordances "deserve to be given a leading role in . . . first philosophy."[8] "First philosophy" deals with the fundamental type of being or substance upon which all others depend, and with the most fundamental causes.[9] Why should affordances enjoy such a prominent place in understanding reality? Sanders writes, "while ontology [the study of being] must be relativized to what different observers can do in terms of affordances, this is no mere matter of what the observer *thinks* or *believes*. It is a function of what the observer *can do*, and this may be as objective a matter as anyone could hope."[10] In other words, affordance relationships simply result in undeniable capabilities that are independent of various philosophies or beliefs involving function or purpose.

Maier is quite forward-thinking in recognizing the primacy of affordances in philosophy. His book, *Affordance Based Design: Theoretical Foundations and Practical Applications*, currently offers the most comprehensive treatment of affordances for engineering, and includes a section on "Application of Affordance Based Design to Biology."[11] Here he summarizes the conflict between "evolutionists" and "creationists"[12] as arising from the tendency to ascribe function or purpose to organisms or their subsystems. He writes, "Hence evolutionists and creationists have a difficult time having an intelligent conversation, even though both may agree on basic scientific facts and perhaps even a belief in a Supreme Being. One of their principal points of contention is the attribution of function and purpose, which goes deeper than just body parts . . . Once again, an affordance based view of these systems can be used to resolve this apparent dilemma."[13]

He goes on to remind us that although the function or purpose of any natural system is inherently *subjectively* defined, the affordances of any natural system can be *objectively* defined. "For example, while an evolutionist may not say that the function of a brain is to think, while a creationist would certainly say that it is, they could both agree to the fact that brains afford thinking . . . Both the possibilities of an intelligent designer (to the chagrin of evolutionists) and of natural design (to the chagrin of creationists) are equally admissible."[14] Thus, initially, affordances provide a neutral way of referring to the inherent capabilities of natural systems, and perhaps this is a step in the right direction. It is when these affordances start stacking up in interesting ways that one may begin to become suspicious, and be drawn to further philosophical conclusions. Let's begin by considering affordances that are too small to see with the naked eye.

Affordances at the Microscopic Level

The ever-popular Mouse Trap game (see Figure 5–1) is an example of a Rube Goldberg machine; a contraption that is deliberately over-engineered to perform a very simple task in a very complicated way, usually including a chain reaction.[15] Although the engineering of a living organism is by no means a simple task,[16] the contraption assembled in playing Mouse Trap helps to illustrate part-to-part affordances that form a series of dependent relationships that ultimately lead to the end-user affordance of being able to catch a "mouse."[17] A similar series of microscopic, dependent relationships provide part-to-part affordances (or dependencies, if you prefer) that ultimately lead to the end-user affordance of life in living organisms.

Biochemistry is the study of chemical processes in living organisms. Molecular biology is the study of the mechanisms by which genetic information encoded in DNA affords life processes. These two fields have made huge progress in the last few years, and we are continually learning more about the mechanisms of life. One of the surprising early discoveries is that all the complexity of life stems from a few simple chemical elements; those atoms that were afforded existence by gravitationally-induced pressures and temperatures within stars.[18] It is now known that just six chemical elements— oxygen, carbon, hydrogen, nitrogen, calcium, and phosphorus—arranged in various combinations,

Figure 5–1   The Mouse Trap Game Illustrates Several Part-to-Part Affordances
Mouse Trap Game Magazine, advert, UK, 1970s / © The Advertising Archives / Bridgeman Images

make up almost 99 percent of the human body. In addition to these six major elements, humans require smaller amounts of about eighteen other elements, such as sodium, chlorine, and iron.[19]

In affording life, these atoms bond to each other in predictable ways to afford the existence of simple but necessary substances such as water and carbon dioxide. Production of more complex biomolecules such as lipids, proteins, acids, vitamins, and hormones are also afforded. The nature of lipids and proteins allow them to combine in forming cell walls that afford organization and protection for the contents of each living cell. Proteins in the cell wall afford communication and transportation through the cell wall.[20] Other proteins inside the cell provide structure for the cell and also afford a kind of "railway system" for communication and transportation within the cell.[21]

The cell is incredibly well-organized to afford all the tasks that it performs. Within each cell is an additional compartment called the nucleus. This region affords further protection for the genetic material of the cell (DNA) and serves as the local control center. The nucleus also affords the construction of ribosomes, which play a central role in affording the construction of proteins. Special proteins called enzymes afford the necessary high-speed chemical reactions for life. Other proteins afford the harvesting of chemical energy, serve in the cell's defense forces, and store and transport molecules, and that's just a few of their roles.[22]

Proteins are made up of long chainlike molecules that fold into precise three-dimensional structures. The resulting shape of each protein determines its interaction with other molecules, and thus its affordances. Proteins form when the machinery of the cell connects smaller molecules called amino acids together in a head-to-tail manner. Cells use twenty different amino acids and each one possesses a specific set of chemical and physical properties. Therefore, each amino acid sequence

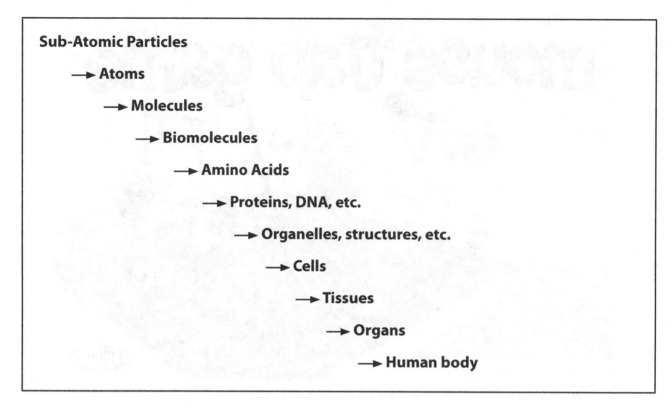

Figure 5–2 Arrows Indicate Just a Few of the Nested Affordances Leading to Human Life
Source: Dominic Halsmer

results in a unique chemical and physical profile that determines how the protein folds, and ultimately determines its shape and unique affordances.[23]

The remarkable truth is that these tiny, nested Lego-like parts afford the complex processes necessary for life. And they do so in an amazing way, with incredible elegance and efficiency, when compared to the kind of affordances that human engineers are able to produce. As microscopes have been refined and reengineered to afford deeper and deeper views into this symphony of harmonious life-promoting activity, researchers have peeled back the layers of the onion;[24] from tissues to cells to subcellular structures to proteins to amino acids to biomolecules to atoms to subatomic particles. These are just a few of the microscopic layers that provide the nested and necessary affordances for life. See Figure 5-2.

Affordances at the Telescopic Level

The story is much the same when we turn our eyes to the heavens. With the help of powerful land- and space-based telescopes, scientists have pierced the sky and pieced together many of the details of our amazing cosmic history. And it is a history that is chocked full of nested affordances for the development and sustenance of complex life on at least one rocky, but water-logged planet. One of the most astonishing events in the history of the universe is the Big Bang itself, which afforded the stuff (matter and energy), and the dimensions (space and time) in which that stuff could interact in very interesting and productive ways. The clumping of matter (mainly hydrogen and helium) to form the first generation of stars after the Big Bang was afforded by a precisely balanced relationship between the inward pull of gravity and the mysterious outward push, or stretching feature, of dark energy.

The resulting pressures and temperatures within these first stars afforded the production of the lighter chemical elements such as carbon, oxygen, and nitrogen. This was accomplished by the collisions of hydrogen and helium atoms at just the right energy levels.[25] This was proposed by scientist Fred Hoyle's hypothesis of stellar nucleosynthesis, which suggested that all the chemical elements had originally been formed from hydrogen and helium.[26] Given this incredible origin for the molecules of life, it might be said that the living world is actually made up of "things that go bump in the night." What is so astonishing is that these kinds of collisions persist beyond stellar evolution, eventually affording complex organisms such as ourselves, who are capable of contemplating our unlikely origin. Subsequent generations of stars produced through supernova explosions afford the heavier elements (such as gold, lead, and uranium) of the periodic table of chemistry, which also serve as an integral part of our world.

Again through the balance of fundamental forces, stars tend to group together in (elliptical, spiral, or irregular) structures called galaxies. These "star parties" afford the necessary combination of heavy elements like carbon and iron to constitute a life-sustaining planet such as Earth; while simultaneously affording a safe region from which to view the dynamics of our universe.[27] Location in the galaxy is critical for achieving the right balance. If you're too far from the center of the galaxy, there won't be enough heavy elements. But if you're too close to the center, harmful levels of radiation prove hazardous to your health.[28] The universe has billions of galaxies that afford habitable regions for potentially life-sustaining planets and solar systems.

Our solar system has several features that contribute to the affordance of advanced life over a long span of time. Our sun is of a size and kind that affords a local environment that is the best habitat for complex life.[29] Our solar system contains nearby planets like Jupiter and Saturn that are large gas giants. These planets afford a relatively quiet neighborhood for Earth since their large masses attract most of the asteroids, directing them away from our planet. Even so, our Moon is now thought to have resulted from a cataclysmic collision between the early Earth and a Mars-sized object. However, this impact appears to have done more good than harm. It deposited vital radioactive elements that contribute to Earth's internal heating, and left a thinner transparent atmosphere that is more conducive to sustained complex life.[30]

The resulting large single moon also contributes to an Earth environment that is supportive of life. The Moon's large mass, its proximity to Earth, and the fact that our planet only has one moon all play a crucial role in stabilizing the tilt of Earth's spin axis. This helps to afford life by protecting Earth from disastrous climate swings.[31] In addition, a less massive or more distant moon would mean weaker ocean tides on Earth. Powerful tidal forces are important for effectively cleansing the coastal seawaters from toxins and enriching them with nutrients.[32] A counter-argument might assert that we should not be surprised that we observe all these affordances for life because if they didn't exist, we wouldn't be around to observe anything different. But it seems that this stance represents the epitome of anti-curiosity (and hence anti-science) as to why these natural nested affordances exist at all; with the effect of affording the strong impression of an ingenious Maker, as stated clearly in Romans 1:20.[33] See Figure 5–3.

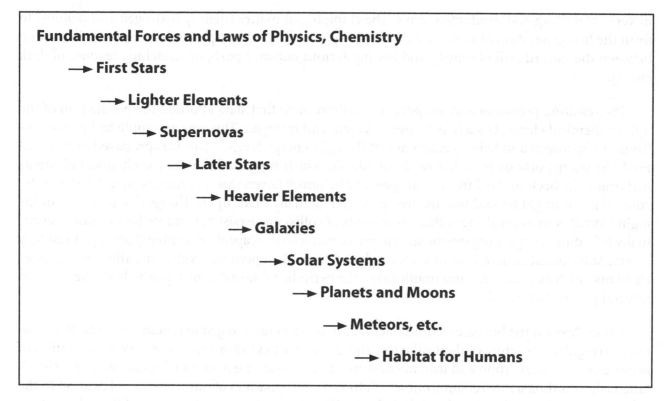

Figure 5–3   Just a Few of the Nested Affordances that Contribute to a Habitat for Humanity
Source: Dominic Halsmer

These are only a few of the affordances we observe at the telescopic level. More information on the many ways that our Moon affords life on Earth can be found in the book, *What if the Moon Didn't Exist? Voyages to Earths that Might Have Been*, by astronomer Neil Comins.[34] More information on the many ways that our universe affords life on Earth at the telescopic level can be found in the book, *Why the Universe is the Way it is*, by astronomer and apologist Hugh Ross.[35] Guillermo Gonzalez and Jay Richards describe the many ways that our cosmos not only affords life, but also affords discovery of how the universe works in their book, *The Privileged Planet: How Our Place in the Cosmos is Designed for Discovery*.[36] But too much looking through telescopes and microscopes can grow wearisome. Let's now consider the affordances we observe with the naked eye.

Affordances at the Macroscopic Level

As pointed out at the beginning of this book, we all experience the good, the bad, and the ugly in this life. But the general ongoing consensus seems to be that, on the whole, life is good. This is obvious from the primal drive for survival and procreation that characterizes all persisting life forms. The foundational element of natural selection and survival-of-the-fittest is that organisms want to live and propagate ongoing life to their descendants. It follows that the positive affordances associated with living outweigh the negative affordances. In other words, life is generally enjoyed by living creatures; otherwise they wouldn't put up with it, and the whole thing would come to a screeching halt!

This state-of-affairs is a direct result of how organisms perceive their immediate environment. As humans, we generally enjoy a wealth of positive affordances at the macroscopic level.

I have fond childhood memories of calling time-out during a football game in our side yard to run into the house for a glass of water. The simple pleasure of quenching a thirst accompanies the fundamental need for humans to remain hydrated; as the saying goes: hydrate or die! Planet Earth sustains an ongoing water cycle with lots of liquid water to afford hydration to its inhabitants.[37] The unique structure of the water molecule affords a multitude of other capabilities, as discussed earlier. While I was enjoyably downing that glass of water, I didn't even realize that all during the game, I was gulping down many cubic meters of air to sustain my multiple touchdown runs. We tend to take the life-sustaining conditions on our planet for granted. The oxygen we need to oxygenate our blood through our lungs is readily available in our atmosphere. In addition, our unusually thin atmosphere affords not only the ability to make fire, but also the opportunity to observe the deeper secrets of our universe, allowing the field of cosmology to flourish, along with its metaphysical implications.

As emphasized in the opening of this chapter, food sources are also generally readily available to earthlings. Here too, we see a delivery system embedded with nested affordances. We don't often take the time to consider the long chain of events that leads to our abundant food supply, but it appears to be an elegantly engineered solution to a difficult energy transfer problem: how to get the necessary energy to sustain complex living organisms for millions of years on an otherwise cold and dark planet? Answer: Goodness gracious, great balls of fire!

Our sun is an amazingly providential ball of burning gas that results in a multitude of affordances for life. We enjoy its light, heat, timing, seasons, and the amazing way that its radiation serves as the foundation for our long-standing global ecosystem. In proper amounts, sunlight affords appropriate levels of vitamin D which helps humans maintain strong bones, among other positive effects. But the major way in which radiant energy gets transferred in a usable fashion to the earth is through an ingenious mechanism called photosynthesis.

During photosynthesis, light from the sun affords radiant energy in the form of photons that green plants can convert to chemical energy, which they use to fuel their growth. In the process, these plants take in water and carbon dioxide, and release oxygen, affording a critical gas necessary for respiration in animals. Since animals produce carbon dioxide during respiration, a stable symbiotic (mutually beneficial) relationship has been afforded on the earth. Green plants also provide an abundant food source for animals. As a result, humans enjoy a wide variety of delicious fruits and meats from both the plant and animal kingdoms.

Before returning to the story of my visit to The Lost World, there is one more capability, largely unique to human beings, which may be the most important affordance of all. It took me a few years to figure this one out, perhaps because as a young man, I focused so much on satisfying my own needs and desires. But after thirty-five years of marriage to my childhood sweetheart and the raising of four wonderful children, I have concluded that the most powerful and beautiful affordance is our ability to love; to seek the good, not just of ourselves, but of the other. My immediate family, especially my wife, has helped me to see this, but love is not just for our "loved ones." Love is most powerful when it is extended universally and unconditionally, and it is most beautiful when it is the most difficult to muster. See Figure 5–4.

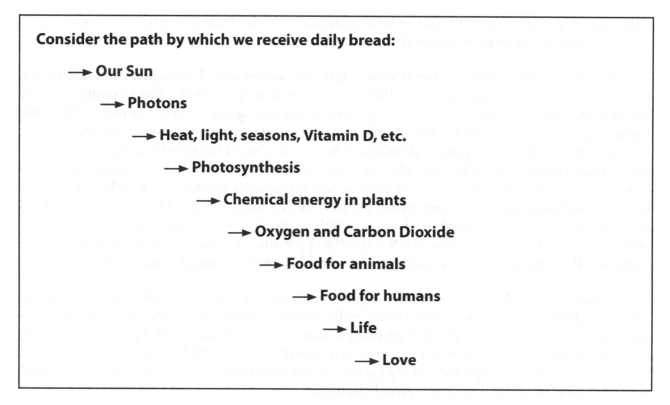

Consider the path by which we receive daily bread:

→ **Our Sun**

→ **Photons**

→ **Heat, light, seasons, Vitamin D, etc.**

→ **Photosynthesis**

→ **Chemical energy in plants**

→ **Oxygen and Carbon Dioxide**

→ **Food for animals**

→ **Food for humans**

→ **Life**

→ **Love**

Figure 5–4   Just a Few of the Nested Affordances that Lead
to the Satisfaction of Human Needs
Source: Dominic Halsmer

COURAGE AND SACRIFICE REWARDED WITH BLACK RASPBERRY PIE

My mouth hung open and out came a joyous shout mixed with laughter, for there standing before me were several huge black raspberry bushes, heavily laden with the largest berries I had ever seen. My first thought, after sampling a few of the berries of course was, "I'm going to need some buckets!" I quickly ran home via the fastest route, taking a straight line through the bean fields. I was pretty certain that Mom couldn't resist making a black raspberry pie if I would bring her enough berries. As I ran in the front door and shared my find between snatched breaths, she happily confirmed my suspicions. She stopped her work to supply me with a couple of buckets and I ran all the way back to The Lost World. It didn't seem so intimidating as I approached it this time. However, I quickly discovered something I had overlooked on my previous visit.

The bushes were being jealously guarded by a blood-thirsty hoard of mosquitoes that seemed to be just as big as the berries. On that particular occasion, it would have been nice to have more than two hands. I was not going to let anything stand in the way of homemade black raspberry pie, but it was a real challenge to fend off the cloud of mosquitoes while filling the buckets. What tasted just as good as the pie that night was the joy of discovery earlier in the day. The earth is bursting forth with good things for us to benefit from and enjoy, and I think our heavenly Father delights in such discoveries. As I walked along the fence row, I can imagine that He was looking down on me and whispering "You're getting warmer; . . . warmer!" I wonder if He somehow had a hand in leading me there that day, since it was unusual that I would go there by myself at such a young age. Was He teaching me that good things can happen when we face our fears and overcome them? Was He teaching me that sometimes sacrifice (like a few mosquito bites) may be necessary to obtain that which is good? I'm astounded at the way the world appears to be engineered to teach us important lessons and fill our lives with good things, like mysteries to be solved, and joy to be discovered, and black raspberries to be baked up in a pie.

STUDY QUESTIONS

1. Describe a time when you faced and overcame a significant fear in your life.
2. What two instruments have dramatically increased the capacity of human sight? And how do they assist in the study of origins?
3. How is it that scientists are able to "look back in time"?
4. How are the heavier chemical elements created? How are the chemical elements similar to Lego blocks?
5. To what degree is this cosmic reverse engineering study objective?
6. What is first philosophy and why do affordances deserve consideration for such a primary status?
7. According to Maier, how might the concept of affordances assist in advancing the conversation on human origins?
8. Describe how nested affordances at the microscopic level contribute to the emergence of living cells.
9. Describe how nested affordances observed with telescopes have contributed to the emergence and sustenance of life.
10. List as many positive affordances as you can that make life enjoyable at the macroscopic level. Do the same for negative affordances that make life challenging. Could any of these negative affordances actually turn out to be positive in the long run?
11. When is love most beautiful? Describe an example of this from your own life.
12. What important lessons have you learned through facing your fears?

ENDNOTES

1. Douglas Adams, *The Hitchhiker's Guide to the Galaxy* (New York: Random House, 1979), 14.

2. Ann Breslin and Alex Montwill, *Let There Be Light: The Story of Light from Atoms to Galaxies* (London: Imperial College Press, 2013), 5.

3. Michael Denton, *Children of Light: The Astonishing Properties of Sunlight that Make Us Possible* (Seattle, WA: Discovery Institute, 2018).

4. It is tempting to say that God is the one who is causing space to expand. And ultimately, I believe this is correct, especially in light of such passages as Job 9:8 (God alone stretches out the heavens . . .). But this is not very helpful to our scientific understanding of the universe, and it can lead to theological problems as well. If we are continually resorting to God as an explanation for things that we don't understand, then as we discover natural mechanisms for these phenomena, are we putting God out of a job? This is known as the "God of the Gaps" fallacy. The Bible also says that in God, all things hold together (Colossians 1:17), so ultimately, he is also responsible for the force of gravity, as well as the other fundamental forces of nature. But that doesn't stop us from digging deeper to uncover natural laws such as the inverse square law that governs the gravitational attraction between two objects. Thus, we should be careful in ascribing natural phenomena to the "hand of God," especially in a scientific context.

5. Dictionary.com.

6. In fact, sometimes part of me wishes Christianity were not true. Then I could do whatever I want, which might not be good in the long run. But if there is no life-after-death, then we just live for the short term anyway. So that would be OK, hence my ambivalence toward the need for Christianity to be true. With regard to the influence of close family members, I love my Christian wife and Christian parents, but I don't think that I would continue to be a Christian just to please them, if I found that the weight of the accumulated evidence dictated apostasy. On the other hand, my experience of Christianity is one of a powerful relationship with the unseen, but very much alive, person of Jesus Christ. Over the years, this relationship has strengthened, and its reality would only be overturned by a significant amount of evidence; say, for example, if the bones of Jesus were discovered and could be reliably identified, effectively negating his bodily resurrection from the dead and eternal life; which is the fundamental and quintessential truth claim of Christianity.

7. John T. Sanders, "Affordances: An Ecological Approach to First Philosophy," in *Perspectives on Embodiment: The Intersections of Nature and Culture*, ed. Gail Weiss and Honi Fern Haber (New York: Routledge, 1999), 122.

8. Sanders, "Affordances," 136.

9. Meriam-webster.com.

10. Sanders, "Affordances," 133.

11. Jonathan Maier, *Affordance Based Design: Theoretical Foundations and Practical Applications* (Saarbrucken, Germany: VDM Verlag, 2011), 165–66.

12. . . . even though "evolutionists" may also be "creationists," and vice versa. See biologos.org for an example of an evangelical Christian foundation that promotes the compatibility of evolution and creation.

13. Maier, *Affordance Based Design*, 166.

14. Maier, *Affordance Based Design*, 166.

15. https://en.wikipedia.org/wiki/Rube_Goldberg.

16. The implications of the enormous challenge of creating artificial life are examined in Fazale Rana, *Creating Life in the Lab: How New Discoveries in Synthetic Biology Make a Case for the Creator* (Grand Rapids, MI: Baker, 2011).

17. A turn of the crank rotates a vertically oriented gear, which meshes with, and affords rotation of, a horizontally oriented gear, which affords motion of a spring-loaded lever, which affords motion to a boot attached to a pendulum, which swings into a bucket, which releases a ball, which rolls down a crooked stairwell and through a curved channel. The ball finally strikes a vertical shaft, affording release of a bigger ball, which falls into a tub, then out of a hole in the bottom of the tub, onto the raised end of a teeter-totter, which affords flight to a plastic man waiting patiently at the other end of the teeter-totter, who subsequently backflips into a tank, which vibrates the foundation of another vertical shaft, which releases a cone-shaped plastic net, which falls on top of the unsuspecting plastic mouse.

18. Helge Kragh, *Matter and Spirit in the Universe* (London: Imperial College Press, 2004), 35, describes the impact these ideas had on the great scientist James Clerk Maxwell, "[Maxwell] was impressed by the fact, as revealed by the spectroscope, that molecules of the same chemical species were all alike and had not changed the slightest 'since the time when nature began.' Uniformity in time as well as uniformity one-to-another strongly indicated that atoms and molecules were created . . . Borrowing an expression from John Herschel, he famously (and with an allusion to natural theology) referred to the molecule as a 'manufactured article.'" It seems that Maxwell also thought of God as a kind of cosmic Engineer.

19. https://en.wikipedia.org/wiki/Biochemistry.

20. Marcos Eberlin, *Foresight: How the Chemistry of Life Reveals Planning and Purpose* (Seattle, WA: Discovery Institute, 2019) argues that the semi-permeable cell membrane is a master work that displays ingenious foresight guided by superb chemical wisdom (p. 19). With a touch of the dramatic, Eberlin adds, "If you were to bid this demanding multifaceted job out to the most technologically advanced engineering firms in the world, their top engineers might either laugh in your face or run screaming into the night. The requisite technology is far beyond our most advanced human know-how." (p. 16) . . . and "the intimation of foresight is powerful. An exquisite phospholipid membrane for the cell apparently had to be anticipated, engineered, and made available just as the cell interior appeared on the scene, lest a skinless cell meet a swift, sure end." (p. 20) . . . and "Some insist it was blind fortune. I disagree and urge us to consider a second possibility—engineering foresight." (p. 21).

21. Fazale Rana, *The Cell's Design: How Chemistry Reveals the Creator's Artistry* (Grand Rapids, MI: Baker, 2008), 39.

22. Rana, *Cell's Design*, 43.

23. Rana, *Cell's Design*, 43.

24. For a fascinating description and implications of the layered feature of the universe down to the subatomic level, see Frank Close, *The New Cosmic Onion: Quarks and the Nature of the Universe* (Boca Raton, FL: Taylor and Francis, 2007).

25. Simon Mitton, *Fred Hoyle: A Life in Science* (Cambridge, UK: Cambridge University Press, 2011), 205–209.

26. It was Fred Hoyle who coined the term "big bang" in a supposedly derisive comment during a BBC radio interview, since he favored the steady-state model of the universe for philosophical reasons. See Mitton, *Fred Hoyle,* 129.

27. Guillermo Gonzalez and Jay W. Richards, *The Privileged Planet: How our Place in the Cosmos is Designed for Discovery* (Washington, DC: Regnery, 2004), 143–68.

28. Gonzalez and Richards, *Privileged Planet,* 159–64.

29. Gonzalez and Richards, *Privileged Planet,* 142.

30. Hugh Ross, *Why the Universe is the Way it is* (Grand Rapids, MI: Baker, 2008), 136.

31. Ross, *Why the Universe,* 80.

32. Ross, *Why the Universe,* 81.

33. For since the creation of the world God's invisible qualities—his eternal power and divine nature—have been clearly seen, being understood from what has been made, so that people are without excuse (NIV).

34. Neil Comins, *What if the Moon Didn't Exist? Voyages to Earths that Might Have Been* (New York: Harper Collins, 1993).

35. Ross, *Why the Universe.*

36. Gonzalez and Richards, *Privileged Planet.*

37. Of course, limitations on such natural resources afford opportunities for cooperation and good stewardship to ensure that everyone's needs are met.

CHAPTER SIX

Abundance of Nested Affordances Point to Ingenuity and Purpose

THE SOFT GOOD EARTH

Being an avid runner who is also getting along in years, I really appreciate the cushioning effect provided by most natural surfaces during a long run. Although surfaces such as dirt, sand, grass, or wild vegetation can be dangerously uneven, maintaining a careful vigilance on foot placement can help to avoid injury. Running on natural surfaces can lead to a strengthening of all lower-body muscles while avoiding the impact injuries associated with hard surfaces. It's also a lot more fun than running on pavement or concrete. It just feels good to run on nice, thick grass, or some other such giving surface.

Actually, my appreciation for the good, soft earth developed at a very young age. One of my earliest memories was the pure joy of going outside to play. I was blessed to grow up (to the extent that this has happened) on five acres among the fertile farmlands of north central Indiana. My dream from a very young age, due mainly to the influence of television and my older brothers, was to become a professional football player. Fortunately, with twelve siblings and assorted cousins and neighbors, it usually wasn't difficult to get a game of tackle or two-hand-touch going.

We made good use of the yard around our house. As a child, I often roamed those acres with a curiosity that was well supplied by the flora and fauna native to that part of Indiana. I remember the satisfying feeling of being intimately familiar with every square foot of our yard. Of course, this intimacy was facilitated by the fact that I helped cut our grass. For me, this began around age five when my mom entrusted me with an old pair of one-handed clippers, and offered me a nickel for every tree I would trim around in our front yard. I have not verified this, but I imagine that there were many small children across the country with that job in the 1960s, and one particular child's hand got so tired of squeezing that clipper again and again that he or she grew up and invented the weed eater. Anyway, I was glad for the opportunity to earn what seemed like a huge amount of money. You see, our front yard had plenty of trees.

But it wasn't long before I was enlisted into a more serious group of grass cutters. In our home, once a child reached grass-cutting age (able to push a mower), they were cheerfully welcomed to participate in our annual springtime ritual known as "divvying up the yard." This typically involved the sketching of an aerial view of our entire property by one of the more senior children, or whoever was acknowledged to have a more artistic gifting. The accuracy of this drawing was important since every "mowable" feature of the yard had to be faithfully represented and appropriately designated. This was done in a sort of disorganized haggling process by which certain portions of the yard were assigned to certain children with various "X"s, "O"s, and "*"s that were marked on the drawing. After much discussion, erasing, revision, crumpling up and starting with a clean sheet, etc., we usually emerged with a clear understanding of what constituted our portion of the kingdom to keep cut. As we headed for the mowers, the carefully crafted schematic remained stuck to our refrigerator with a magnet for reference, in times of inevitable future disputes.

I think we felt a pride and enthusiasm for cutting our grass, in the same way that baseball groundskeepers or golf greenskeepers sense. I know that for me, it was important to keep the yard in good shape for the purpose of having nicely kept and multipurpose playing fields. Our front yard made an ideal baseball, softball, or kickball field, having appropriate trees for first and third bases. (The mat from in front of our front door served as a welcome change when sliding into second.) Our side yard on the north contained our enormous swing set and slide, leaving just enough room for a run-up to the high jump pit under the apple tree between the vegetable garden and the rhubarb patch.

But it was our side yard on the south that held a special place in my little heart. Being fairly large and rectangular in shape, it served as an excellent gridiron (football field). There were no lines on the field but everyone knew where the boundaries were. The sidelines were understood to be the side of the swimming pool shed on the north, and the large shagbark hickory tree on the south. The goal lines were more important, clearly marked by an invisible line extending from the edge of the house on the east, and another invisible line extending from the edge of the pool yard fence on the west. The end lines, which took on vital importance during scoring attempts through the air, were the huge forsythia bushes on the east, and the start of Grandma McCarthy's yard on the west. The start of Grandma's yard was easy to discern by the line of fir trees and trampled flowers. (Sorry, Grandma.) Both sets of grandparents lived behind us, as did our cousins, which greatly enriched our family life.

I still have vivid memories of flying out the back door and down the steps in wild anticipation of a two-hand-touch or tackle football game. In a few steps I would reach the field and dive for joy into the thick grass, rolling in celebration of the good soft earth that gently welcomed my impacts. When my older sister Lilly and I were of elementary school age, but still too young to be of much use on offense, we were assigned the important job of rushing the quarterback, which we honed to a fine art. We were known as the "gruesome twosome," and our older brothers shivered at the thought of our vicious onslaught. At least, that was the myth they perpetuated, and we reveled in our dubious ferocity.

Through all those years, I don't ever remember getting injured simply by falling to the ground. I remember getting the wind knocked out of me by falling on the ball or running into another person. But the ground was generally soft and forgiving, especially if one was accustomed to falling down, which I did on almost every play, often for no particular reason. A game was particularly satisfying if the occasion arose to attempt a diving catch. It was a wonderful thing to be able to fall to the ground without fear of serious injury. This effect was exaggerated whenever the grass was particularly deep, or if we were playing in the snow, wearing heavy winter coats. Often, we would celebrate a deep snowfall with a game of tackle football in the middle of winter. Of course, things were different when I went off to St. Boniface elementary school, since our recess (recreation time) took place on a concrete parking lot. But old habits are hard to break, as will become evident near the end of this chapter.

Affordances Are Readily Interpreted

In the next chapter, we will explore how engineers often identify and interpret affordances through a process known as reverse engineering. But for now, let's consider what may or may not be communicated with affordances. When analyzing a complex device, engineers look for relationships between the various pieces that result in some new capability or potential action (affordance). When designing such a device, engineers use their knowledge, creativity, and resourcefulness to exploit relationships in nature, thereby producing valuable affordances for their customers. This is why engineering students benefit by taking several science courses in college (physics, chemistry, material science, etc.). They need to know how nature works if they are to put nature to work for themselves and the rest of the human race.

Engineers do exactly this by producing a variety of products that generally make life better for people. If these products are well-engineered, they readily communicate their usefulness and desirability to the potential customer by clearly presenting the potential positive affordance or affordances to be enjoyed. In addition, consumers are able to assess the quality of these affordances by observing the craftsmanship, materials, and "attention to detail" present in the engineered product. Often, an off-brand or "knock-off" imitation will not measure up to the original product because it was not engineered to the same high-quality standards. This can easily result in lower-quality affordances. I've enjoyed building Lego kits with our children for years, but one Christmas I decided to save some money and try another brand of connecting building blocks. I regretted my decision because it quickly became evident that the plastic was of a lower quality, and the interference (press) fit was not as precisely engineered. As a result, the blocks did not go together as well, or stay together as well as the original Legos. The off-brand blocks still afforded building, but the affordance was of a lesser quality.

As mentioned previously, affordances can also be positive or negative. Smartphones provide an incredible number of positive affordances, but they can also lead to some negative situations. They have a way of capturing and holding our attention, even when our attention may be desperately needed elsewhere, as when operating heavy machinery such as an automobile. In addition, since it is more difficult to communicate emotions while texting, missed connotations and misunderstandings can more easily occur than in verbal dialogue. Hence, smartphones provide such positive affordances as communication, access to information, and photography, but also contribute to negative affordances such as distractibility and miscommunication.

There is no question that the natural world presents us with a long list of affordances that make it possible for us to enjoy life on this planet. This can be interpreted in a variety of ways. Some suggest that our life-sustaining universe is just a brute fact, about which we should not bother to be curious.[1] Others suggest that humans are just the lucky recipients of these vital and vibrant conditions, supposing that there are many more universes (the multiverse idea) besides our own. This makes it more likely that there would be at least one universe (our own) with the right natural laws and conditions for life.[2] Now there's nothing inherently atheistic about the multiverse theory, but there's something glaringly absent from both of these interpretations. And it is the recognition that in general, affordances are intentionally provided; especially when they show up in large quantities and in nested configurations. As such, an appropriate human response should be one of gratitude, appreciation, and thankful recognition to the provider. Or at the very least, curiosity and exploration as to the origin of all these interconnected strings of affordances.

Numerous Nested Affordances Point beyond Nature

In his paper, "Affordances are Signs," philosopher John Pickering recognizes a "primordial intentionality"[3] behind the complex configurations of matter and energy in the universe. And this recognition arises out of an appreciation for the affordances that exist in nature. He writes, "Organism and [environment] are integrated by the exchange of meaning. Affordances are behavioral meanings; they are signs to an organism that actions are possible."[4] He proposes that the application of semiotics (the study of signs and symbols as elements of communicative behavior[5]) to natural systems provides "a means for unifying science,"[6] especially with regard to questions of origins.

In concluding his paper, Pickering quotes Jesper Hoffmeyer, who writes, "The world is full of subjects and something must have created them. But latent within that 'something' there must, inevitably, be 'someone.' Subjectivity has its roots in the cosmos and, at the end of the day, the repression of this aspect of our world is not a viable proposition."[7] Pickering returns to his original question, "How can feeling and thought exist if there is only matter in motion?" and answers, "by recognizing that feeling and thought are primordially present in matter."[8] Since humans "make the effort to find meaning in their surrounding and their experience,"[9] they tune in to the idea that affordances point beyond the methodologically restricted realm of science to the existence of a Maker.

Early in the twentieth century, broadly-thinking scientists like Lawrence Henderson were beginning to recognize the amazing interdependency of various features of the universe for life. In his 1913 book, *The Fitness of the Environment*, he concludes, "The properties of matter and the course of cosmic evolution are now seen to be intimately related to the structure of the living being and to its activities; they become, therefore, far more important in biology than has been previously suspected. For the whole evolutionary process, both cosmic and organic, is one, and the biologist may now rightly regard the universe in its very essence as biocentric."[10] Henderson's work was an early version of what has now become known as the fine-tuning problem: How is it that the universe appears to be specifically engineered to facilitate the emergence of life?

The Fitness of the Environment has become a classic, and was celebrated recently by the publication of a follow-on work by several famous scientists. *The Fitness of the Cosmos for Life: Biochemistry and Fine-Tuning* looks at the delicate balance between chemistry and the prevailing conditions in the universe that permit complex chemical networks and life-supporting structures to exist. In this book, biologist Christian de Duve writes, "We live in a biofriendly world. Were it otherwise, we wouldn't be around. The question is, therefore, how biofriendly is it? Physicists have addressed this question and have come to the conclusion that if any of the fundamental physical constants were a little smaller or a little larger than they are, the universe would be very different from what it is and unable to produce or harbor living organisms."[11] Concepts such as fitness and fine-tuning are related to the idea of an engineered universe, and can be reframed in terms of engineered affordances that exhibit a nested configuration in nature.

Also from *The Fitness of the Cosmos for Life*, biologist Simon Conway Morris writes, "[Microscopic] organisms appear on the whole as though they had been precisely engineered. They operate as though aware of their environment, and invariably they are able to modify it . . . In addition, they are capable of sophisticated computational exercises . . . No matter how familiar we are with these factors, we too easily take them for granted. Yet the fine-tuning of organisms is entirely extraordinary, as even a glance at a living cell and its biochemical intricacies will confirm: machine-like, but unlike any machine we can build."[12] The emergence of machine-like biostructures and organisms that exhibit nested affordances speaks of an engineering influence that underlies the cosmos. These discoveries carry with them the important connotations of ingenuity and purpose.

Affordances Are Signs of Ingenuity and Purpose

In his contribution to *The Fitness of the Cosmos for Life*, theologian John Haught writes, "What purpose means, at the very minimum, is 'the actualizing of value'—that is, of what appears self-evidently good . . . Thus a universe that appears to be in the process of bringing about such value-laden actualities as life, consciousness, freedom, creativity, and [the appreciation of] beauty, along with beings endowed with a capacity for reasonableness, selfless love, and promise keeping, could be said to have an overarching purpose, provided, of course, that these achievements have been intended."[13] Notice that his list of valuable actualities are affordances; good things that are afforded by the makeup and interaction of the elements of our universe.

It should be clear that the force of this evidence from engineering does not proceed from a few specific instances (although detailed examples help to illustrate the idea), but permeate the entire fabric of the cosmos. Theologian F. R. Tennant writes, "The forcibleness of Nature's suggestion that she is the outcome of intelligent design lies not in particular cases of adaptedness in the world . . . [but] consists rather in the conspiration of innumerable causes to produce, by their united and reciprocal action, and to maintain, a general order of nature."[14] This order of nature seems to be for the purpose of producing valuable affordances such as life.

The force of the evidence is compounded when the general quality of these ingenious affordances is considered. Ingenuity is defined as skill or cleverness in devising or combining,[15] and this is evident in nature. An engineering design is considered to be ingenious when a few simple elements are skillfully combined to produce something that may be complex, but is still functional, elegant, efficient, and beautiful. Due largely to discoveries of the twentieth century, scientists, engineers, and mathematicians generally agree that our universe exhibits this characteristic, as described in the groundbreaking work, *The Anthropic Cosmological Principle*, by physicists John Barrow and Frank Tipler.

They write, "One of the most important results of twentieth-century physics has been the gradual realization that there exist invariant properties of the natural world and its elementary components which render the gross size and structure of virtually all its constituents quite inevitable. The size of stars and planets, and even people, are neither random nor the result of any Darwinian selection process from a myriad of possibilities. These, and other gross features of the universe are the consequences of necessity; they are manifestations of the possible equilibrium states between competing forces of attraction and compulsion. The intrinsic strengths of these controlling forces of nature are determined by a mysterious collection of pure numbers that we call the *constants of nature*."[16] There are only a few of these constants, and the mathematical equations that govern all the various phenomena in the universe can easily fit on one side of an 8.5x11 inch sheet of paper. The impression of incredible ingenuity is striking.

In discussing the superb performance of feedback control systems within the living cell, engineer Bryant Shiller writes, "The fact that all of this works so well (and at all) speaks to the issue of 'excellence' of applied form and function as we perceive it. Indeed, as amateur engineers (the role each of you assumed when you began this inquiry) the fathoming of just some of the complex functioning of, what is after all, just your average (and dirt cheap) eukaryotic cell has to be a humbling experience. No less so for experienced engineers (and biologists) for whom just grasping and appreciating the feat of miniaturization that is the living cell represents a formidable challenge. Then, of course, couple all this wonder with the economies and efficiencies involved and one is left literally breathless—what human engineers can only envy."[17] Hence, the positive affordances associated with life processes exhibit an amazing ingenuity. The implication is of a Maker who possesses exquisite engineering expertise.

The Invitational Nature of Affordances

Several researchers have picked up on the idea that affordances not only provide action possibilities, but can also *invite* behavior.[18] Psychologist Rob Withagen writes, "When actively exploring the environment, the agent is attracted or repelled by some of its affordances, and the ensuing behavior is partly the result of these invitations."[19] Julian Kiverstein expands on this theme in recognizing the continuous process of maintaining positive affordances as the basis for purposeful behavior in a meaningful environment. He writes, "Affordances are in flux and unfold in the landscape through the ongoing patterns of activity of individuals responding to the invitation of relevant affordances. Through these patterns of activity affordances set up the conditions for their own continuation. Molar [or purposeful] behavior should be thought of as fundamentally anticipatory—individuals are responsive to the direction of the process which they help to sustain, and keep alive through their activities.[20] At least for human beings, this state-of-affairs is a direct result of free will and our ability to reflect on possibilities (reflexivity), but the environment also plays a critical role in presenting these invitations.

Pickering illustrates this point when he writes, "The characteristic reflexivity of human cognition means that we are not only able to perceive the world as it is, that is, to perceive the affordances that actually surround us, but also to perceive affordances that do not yet exist, that is, to perceive the world as if it were otherwise. When we take a rock and modify it with blows until it functions as a blade, we do just that. We not only perceive what is, but also what may be and hence we may take meaningful, intentional action to bring it about if we so choose."[21] This ability to use creativity, resourcefulness, knowledge, and wisdom to make improvements to our environment is consistent with the Judeo-Christian understanding that we bear the image of God. We can engineer things (at least to some degree) because God is the ultimate engineer, and we are made in His image.

Think about the incredible string of nested affordances that exist in the mind-body system that allows human beings to engage in engineering activities. A variety of sense organs (eyes, ears, nose, and skin) afford an enormous amount of valuable information about the outside world. A powerful information processor (brain) receives this information and affords the ability to form beliefs about the nature of the world. Part of the brain serves as a memory bank that, based on these beliefs, affords conscious reasoning about past, present, and future events. Other parts of the brain afford our ability to have desires and purposes, which we reason to sometimes be good, but sometimes be evil. Another part of the brain serves as a processor to turn these desires and purposes into limb and other voluntary movements, which afford our ability to impact the world around us, for good or for ill.[22]

Beyond this, recent discoveries in the field of epigenetics show that the decisions we make about how to live our lives not only end up affecting who we become as people, but also affect the lives and tendencies of our children and future descendants.[23] Even without getting into the nitty-gritty biological details that make all this possible, it seems clear that this is an amazing set of nested affordances. Figure 6–1 illustrates the feedback nature of these affordances. As we believe the truth and pursue the good, we perceive that the actions we are taking tend to have a positive influence on who we become, and how we affect others and the world. This has the effect of inviting us to continue on in this positive direction.

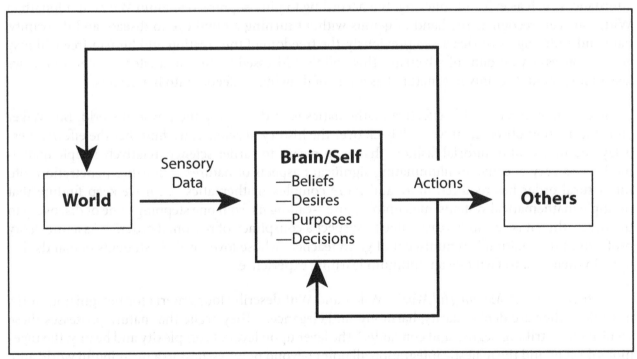

Figure 6–1   The Feedback Nature of the Mind/Body/World System
Source: Dominic Halsmer

At this point, philosopher of religion Richard Swinburne asks a very good question: "Why are there not just any laws of nature, but [instead we discover] laws of a particular kind such that together with the initial matter-energy at the time of the 'Big Bang' would lead to the evolution of human bodies?"[24] He argues that such laws and initial conditions facilitating the emergence of human bodies with such a remarkable set of affordances is "very improbable *a priori*, but fairly probable if there is a God who brought it about."[25] One of the most remarkable things about these affordances is that they invite us to choose; choose between good or evil, love or hate, care or neglect, activism or apathy, wisdom or foolishness, faith or unbelief.[26] And the life that results is a testimony to the wisdom of those choices, and a legacy for the lives that will follow in that person's biological wake.

Somebody up There Loves Us

As a husband and father of four adult children, and now two grandchildren, I know a little bit about love and the handing down of a legacy. Like nearly all married couples, my wife and I have had to make some hard choices over the years. Often, we have to deny our own selfish desires in order to choose love and care for each other instead of something (or someone) that may seem more gratifying or comforting at the moment. In so doing, over time we have "engineered" a healthy environment that affords love and security for the family as a whole. When we are successful at making such wise choices, it seems that our love grows deeper and more beautiful. As a result, we sense an invitation to invest in each other more fully, get to know each other even better, and enjoy each other all the more. It seems that mankind's experience of the universe offers an interesting parallel to our family situation.

The layers of positive affordances embedded in the universe provide us with the gifts of life and love that we celebrate and enjoy. To be fair, we should also acknowledge the existence of negative affordances such as evil and suffering. But according to philosophers Benjamin Wiker and Jonathan Witt, "one can recognize the hand of genius without turning a blind eye to disease and deformity, pain and suffering."[27] As discussed previously, the freedom of the creation and human free will may entail a necessary amount of adversity. This will be addressed further in a later chapter. But as we learn more about the universe, nature has a way of drawing us deeper into her secrets.

Recall how unreasonably effective mathematics is in describing the physical world. But Wiker and Witt further observe, "if we look back over the history of science, we find that the effectiveness is layered in a kind of tutorial fashion; that is, in regard to earlier science, relatively simple mathematics was very effective in illuminating significant aspects of nature . . . Further penetration into the natural order has required more and more complex mathematics . . . if we keep finding that multiple mathematical systems 'map onto' nature—calling us from one steppingstone of discovery to the next—then it is certainly reasonable to suspect a conspiracy of reasoned order."[28] As a university professor, this situation is reminiscent of good teachers whose love for their students demands that they do their best to facilitate an optimum learning experience.

In their book, *A Meaningful World*, Wiker and Witt describe four criteria for recognizing works of genius. They are depth, clarity, harmony, and elegance.[29] They argue that nature possesses these qualities to a striking degree, and conclude, "The layer upon layer of complexity and beauty, the ingenious designs and the majestic integration all point beyond pointlessness to a meaningful world and, more than this, to the genius of nature."[30] Chemist Marcos Eberlin, in his book, *Foresight: How the Chemistry of Life Reveals Planning and Purpose*, extends this list of criteria for recognizing ingenious engineering by adding a fifth element: foresight. He writes, "All of those marvels depend on deeper levels of foresight. Science has revealed that Earth and the cosmos display layer upon layer of features essential to life."[31] Because of the way these valuable and high-quality affordances seem to be directed specifically at human beings, I argue that they are the expression of a loving Mastermind who desires to share his love with all people. And this masterful Maker invites us into a deeper knowledge of who he is and what he does through the affordances he provides.

KEEPING CONNECTIONS WITH OUR NATURAL ENVIRONMENT

As a youngster, change was often difficult for me. Riding the bus away from home to elementary school was a big challenge. Fortunately, I had many older siblings to help me cope. In first grade, I started attending St. Boniface Catholic School. But I was a very nervous first-grader and cried easily, like whenever the teacher would leave the room! That's probably why I suggested we play football at recess. It was something we did at home and as a result, I think it made me feel closer to home.

A few classmates and I could quickly recruit enough kids for a game simply by marching around at recess, arm in arm, repeatedly chanting in a roughly musical manner, "WHO WANTS TO PLAY FOOTBAAAALL?" I can still remember the silly little tune we employed. I'm sure we must have sounded like a broken record. But one by one, kids would become persuaded to join in the march and add to the ever increasing volume of our siren song, which we promptly abandoned in favor of the advertised activity.

Unfortunately we had recess on the paved church parking lot since we didn't have any grassy fields on which to play. However, I was fairly stuck in my ways, and I only knew one way to play football. I eventually learned to adjust my play to a less forgiving surface, but opportunities to make a diving catch don't come along every day, and they are hard to pass up. I remember making one such rather painful catch in the parking lot, and then laying there clutching the ball, looking up at my classmates staring at me in disbelief and amazement. It reminded me of that time Curious George was on the run from the angry painters. He jumped from the fire escape, expecting his fall to be broken by the soft ground of his jungle home, but instead he broke his leg on the hard city sidewalk and ruined everything![32] I could relate to that poor little guy.

Although the overwhelming majority of my current existence is spent pushing the bottoms of my feet against unnaturally hard surfaces, I still revel in those times in the yard, at the park, or in the woods. It is then that I feel the urge to run and jump and catch the uncatchable ball. It is then that I feel like a kid again. God has not left himself without testimony in this regard (Acts 14:17). The comfort and pleasures we enjoy on this remarkably well-suited planet were provided by a master design engineer, and they are only a shadow of what He has prepared for our future.

The soft good earth is just one of many examples of multifunctional and integrated systems resulting in positive affordances that have been engineered for our benefit. The earth serves as a stable platform for our activities. Its makeup is intimately linked to the moderate temperatures we continually enjoy. It provides a medium for growing vegetation, and producing all-important oxygen and food. It is home to our friends in the animal kingdom, and a wonderful playground for mankind.

Human engineers come up with new surfaces, such as Astro-Turf, but it's hard to beat good old grass when it comes to football, running, and a multitude of other activities. I hope and pray that we're smart enough to allow large portions of natural surfaces to persist in our living areas in the future. Perhaps maintaining this connection with the good earth will encourage a connection with our Maker, in addition to making space for aging runners to go easy on their joints.

STUDY QUESTIONS

1. What affordances did you find particularly enjoyable as a child?
2. Under what conditions is it likely that affordances have been intentionally provided? What would be appropriate human responses in this case?
3. What is it about nested affordances that point to an intelligence beyond nature?
4. In what sense is the universe biocentric, or biofriendly?
5. How is the idea of natural nested affordances related to the fine-tuning of the universe?
6. From Haught's discussion of purpose, how do nested affordances lead to thoughts of a purposeful universe?
7. Considering the definition of "ingenuity," how do nested affordances lead to thoughts of an ingenious universe?
8. How do free will and human reflexivity relate to the invitational nature of nested affordances?
9. How do the nested affordances of the mind/body system lead to considerations of a divine engineer who wants to present us with significant life-changing choices?
10. Describe an example of how layers of natural affordances are presented in tutorial fashion.
11. Describe examples for each of the four criteria that suggest that the universe is the work of a genius.
12. How does spending time in nature help us "tune in" to our Maker? What natural spaces do you particularly enjoy?

ENDNOTES

1. Richard Dawkins, *The God Delusion* (New York: Houghton Mifflin, 2008).
2. Leonard Susskind, *The Cosmic Landscape: String Theory and the Illusion of Intelligent Design* (New York: Time Warner, 2006).
3. John Pickering, "Affordances are Signs," *tripleC* 5, no. 2 (2007): 74.
4. Pickering, "Affordances are Signs," 72.
5. www.dictionary.com.
6. Pickering, "Affordances are Signs," 72.
7. Jesper Hoffmeyer, *Signs of Meaning in the Universe* (Bloomington, IN: Indiana University Press, 1996), 57–58.

8. Pickering, "Affordances are Signs," 73.

9. Pickering, "Affordances are Signs," 74.

10. Lawrence Joseph Henderson, *The Fitness of the Environment: An Inquiry into the Biological Significance of the Properties of Matter* (New York: MacMillan, 1913), 312.

11. Christian de Duve, "How Biofriendly is the Universe?" in *The Fitness of the Cosmos for Life: Biochemistry and Fine-Tuning*, ed. John D. Barrow et al. (Cambridge: Cambridge University Press, 2008), 169.

12. Simon Conway Morris, "Tuning into the Frequencies of Life: A Roar of Static or a Precise Signal" in *The Fitness of the Cosmos for Life: Biochemistry and Fine-Tuning*, ed. John D. Barrow et al. (Cambridge: Cambridge University Press, 2008), 213.

13. John F. Haught, "Is Fine-Tuning Remarkable" in *The Fitness of the Cosmos for Life: Biochemistry and Fine-Tuning*, ed. John D. Barrow et al. (Cambridge: Cambridge University Press, 2008), 32.

14. F. R. Tennant, *Philosophical Theology*, Vol. 2 (Cambridge: Cambridge University Press, 1956), 79.

15. www.merriam-webster.com.

16. John Barrow and Frank J. Tipler, *The Anthropic Cosmological Principle* (Oxford: Oxford University Press, 1986), 5.

17. Bryant M. Shiller, *Origin of Life: The Fifth Option* (Victoria, BC: Trafford Publishing, 2004), 248.

18. Rob Withagen, Harjo J. de Poel, Duarte Araujo, and Gert-Jan Pepping, "Affordances Can Invite Behavior: Reconsidering the Relationship between Affordances and Agency," *New Ideas in Psychology* 30 (2012): 250–58.

19. Withagen et al, "Affordances Can Invite Behavior," 257.

20. Julian Kiverstein, Ludger van Dijk, and Erik Rietveld, "The Field and Landscape of Affordances: Koffka's Two Environments Revisited," *Synthese*, 20 March 2019, https://doi.org/10.1007/s11229-019-02123-x.

21. Pickering, "Affordances are Signs," 73.

22. Richard Swinburne, *The Existence of God*, 2nd ed. (Oxford: Oxford University Press, 2004), 169.

23. David S. Moore, *The Developing Genome: An Introduction to Behavioral Epigenetics* (Oxford: Oxford University Press, 2015).

24. Swinburne, *Existence of God*, 172.

25. Swinburne, *Existence of God*, 172.

26. According to the rock band, Rush, "If you choose not to decide, you still have made a choice," from "Freewill," *Permanent Waves* (1980).

27. Benjamin Wiker and Jonathan Witt, *A Meaningful World: How the Arts and Sciences Reveal the Genius of Nature* (Downers Grove, IL: InterVarsity Press, 2006), 28.

28. Wiker and Witt, *Meaningful World*, 103–04.

29. Wiker and Witt, *Meaningful World*, 75–80.

30. Wiker and Witt, *Meaningful World*, 27.

31. Marcos Eberlin, *Foresight: How the Chemistry of Life Reveals Planning and Purpose* (Seattle, WA: Discovery Institute, 2019), 26.

32. H. A. Rey, *Curious George Takes a Job* (New York: Houghton Mifflin, 1947).

PART III

Affordance-Based Reverse Engineering

PART III

Affordance-Based Reverse Engineering

CHAPTER SEVEN

Reverse Engineering of Natural Systems

RECONSTRUCTING DAVID FROM THE THINGS HE HAD MADE

I woke up and had just wiped the sleep from my eyes when my mind enthusiastically recaptured a most important fact: "David is getting home today!" Growing up with ten older siblings can make for a pretty exciting childhood. My brother David was eleven years older than me, but I seemed to develop a strong affinity for him even as a small child. As a young man, David was very athletic, creative, and always working on some new project, like the home-grown parasailing effort described earlier. So you can imagine my dismay a few years earlier when I learned that he was leaving home to join the Marines. I had just turned nine years old, and I found out that he would be gone for three years. That's a long time for a nine-year-old; well, a third of a lifetime from my young perspective!

And you can also understand my excitement on the day of his return. He had been serving as a United States Embassy Guard in Bucharest, Romania, and The Hague, Netherlands, so we had had very little contact with him due to this long-distance assignment. Even so, my affection for him had only grown stronger in his absence. This may seem curious since the length of his time away represented fully one-third of my entire life span up to that point. Indeed, I might have forgotten him altogether were it not for the many creative works he left behind. I came across these treasures periodically, and they reminded me of him; not only of him, but of the kind of person he was: gentle, positive, confident, kind, caring, fun-loving, and a skilled craftsman who loved to turn his many mental conceptions into actual physical contraptions.

One of my earliest memories was the discovery of his many model rockets kept in a secret laboratory "down the basement." Those early launches during my elementary school days always had me brimming over with excitement. But it wasn't long before David had developed a hand-held rocket launcher; kind of a homemade bazooka constructed from old Folgers coffee cans and various leftover parts from Dad's workshop. I remember the day he tested it out by firing a metal-tipped model rocket from our front yard at the big old red barn across the road about 50 yards away. It turns out that he *could* hit the broad side of a barn with that gadget! And put a good-sized dent in it. That old green bazooka hanging on the wall seemed to catch my attention every time I walked through our garage for years after it was engineered.

David also enjoyed building very detailed models of aircraft and spacecraft and photographing them in realistic settings. The original *Star Trek* was one of our favorite TV shows, and he built a very impressive and photogenic model of the Starship *USS Enterprise*. A fledgling space program was at the forefront of our national consciousness back then, so he also built a model of the *Gemini* space capsule, complete with America's first space walker, Astronaut Ed White. To simulate this great historic event, he suspended the capsule and tethered astronaut with thread from our basement ceiling, along with some tiny balls of aluminum foil for stars. After getting the lighting just right, he carefully snapped some photographs that were hard to distinguish from the real thing! He even filmed a rendition of the sinking of the battleship *Bismarck* on the surface of the pond in our back horse pasture, including the ignition of timed explosive charges. This was my absolute favorite of all our "home movies," but our horse didn't much care for it.

While David was gone, I also discovered some amazing photos he had shot of an incredibly detailed World War I-era British aerodrome, suffering a withering attack by the Red Baron and his cohorts from the Flying Circus. He had laid out some green felt and set the whole thing up on, and above, our ping-pong table in the basement, after finishing a set of WWI plastic model aircraft and carefully hand-painting some tiny, plastic, British infantrymen. My favorite part was the crashed plane in the middle of the aerodrome, complete with the injured pilot, attempting to crawl free of the burning wreckage, leaving a trail of blood. (Please forgive a ten-year-old boy's ignorance of the horrors of real war.)[1] At some point during David's military service, while rummaging through the basement, I also retrieved a dusty old box that was well hidden among the rafters. My opening of that box was something akin to discovering a chest of gold coins and sparkling jewels. To my delight, upon pulling back the protective layer of cotton, I discovered that I had unwittingly come across the magnificent set of toy soldiers David had so carefully prepared for the aerodrome diorama![2] Not having much respect for property rights at that age, I kept them for my own, and played with them until the paint had virtually worn clean off.

At other times I would roam around outside, exploring our five acres or the attached parcels of land where my grandparents and cousins lived. On one occasion while trekking through the back pasture, I came across a narrow patch of cement that seemed to stretch off indefinitely in opposite directions. This was curious. It was like a straight city sidewalk smackdab in the middle of our horse pasture! I followed it in one direction until it ended abruptly, not far from one of my grandparents' trailers. So I turned and followed it in the other direction. This time, the cement trail ended in a kind of wedge-shaped depression in the ground, surrounded by huge bags of foam rubber, like enormous overstuffed pillows where the Jolly Green Giant could rest his massive head. I also noticed two tall poles with small pegs sticking out near their tops, standing to either side. Now it was all starting to come together, and I remembered what this was. David had constructed a full-sized pole-vault pit and runway, complete with a cement box in which to plant the pole at takeoff.

Since we lived several miles from Central Catholic High School, David reasoned that he would get more time to practice vaulting if he could literally do it in his own backyard. And this reasoning had paid off, since he soon held the school record, vaulting twelve and a half feet in an era when the metal vaulting poles did not bend to any considerable degree. This achievement fit neatly with my recollection that David was also best at forming plays and quarterbacking when we played football in our side yard. And these are just a few of my many boyhood memories about my excellent brother David.

During his absence, all the things David had made and the stories of the things he had accomplished had a way of keeping him alive and almost present for me during those three years. I remember telling stories about him and sharing some of his artifacts with some of my friends from school. In a sense we were reconstructing, or reverse engineering, who David was based on things he had made and done over the years. He certainly was (and still is) a real cool dude, and I admired him immensely (and still do). That's why I was so excited on the day he came home. But before I finish this story, let's take a closer look at the science, art, and philosophy of reverse engineering as applied to natural systems.

A Brief History of Reverse Engineering

We have seen that the universe exhibits a long string of nested affordances for life; and not just simple life, but the kind of life that can stand up, look back, and ponder from whence it came; the kind of life that has the power to make good and evil choices that influence the world, others, and, ultimately, our own destiny. This is the kind of life that has the unique ability to love: "To act intentionally, in sympathetic response to others (including God), to promote overall well-being."[3] Love is universally considered by the human race to be of great value. When a series of complex nested affordances results in something of such great value, the implication is that there is a skilled engineer at work. And the best way to understand an engineered system is with a reverse engineering approach. Thus, in our attempts to make sense of the universe, "hacking" the cosmos represents a rational and reasonable response to the scientific evidence that is unhindered by methodological restrictions.[4]

Reverse engineering is a time-tested approach centered on the idea that humans learn best from experience. When confronted with a complex system, the best way to understand how it works and why it exists is to explore it, often by taking it apart. This "'taking apart,' or dissection, may be quite literal and physical, or figurative and conceptual."[5] In the case of living organisms, physical dissection has been found to be indispensable. But the universe as a whole requires a more conceptual dissection and analysis. Indeed, anthropologist Ian Tattersall points out, "Human beings alone, it seems, mentally dissect the world into a multitude of discrete symbols, and combine and recombine those symbols in their minds to produce hypotheses of alternative possibilities."[6] The mindset and methodology of reverse engineering is proposed for exploring the hypothesis of an engineered universe.

This method, also known as "reverse problem-solving," has certainly been in use for a very long time. One of the most recent books on reverse engineering, by Robert Messler, describes one of the earliest known examples involving the Great Pyramid of Khufu in Egypt around 2560 BC. During construction, workers noticed a crack forming in the 50-ton granite beam across the ceiling of the king's burial chamber deep in the core of the pyramid. This imperfection indicated that a redesign was needed to deflect the huge load away from the center of this beam and out toward the supports at each side of the chamber. With some repositioning of structural elements, this was accomplished, and the Great Pyramid was saved.[7] This example illustrates the importance of attending to the relationship between the engineer and his or her creation. In this case, the pyramid was crying out (through the crack) to its creators for help! Fortunately, the Egyptian engineers and architects had the wisdom to listen and respond appropriately.

An early and well-known example of reverse engineering of natural systems arose out of the Colosseum in ancient Rome as a result of the gruesome injuries inflicted during gladiator games. Galen of Pergamon (CE 129–ca. 200), who is known as the "father of modern medicine," learned much from the dissection of animals and deceased humans (many from the arena). Leonardo da Vinci (CE 1452–1519) also conducted reverse engineering studies on biological systems, fueling his great genius and extraordinary understanding of nature.[8] These studies not only contributed to his knowledge of medicine but also to his development of advanced technologies such as automatic mechanisms and flying machines. After extensive study of the human body he concluded, "The human foot is a masterpiece of engineering and a work of art." Thus, da Vinci expressed appreciation for the beautiful and elegant functionality exhibited by living systems. A few hundred years later, anatomist Henry Gray brought this reverse engineering project to a magnificent culmination with the comprehensive and detailed illustrations in *Gray's Anatomy of the Human Body*, initially published in 1858, but still in use today.[9]

The many military conflicts of the twentieth century escalated the practice of reverse engineering in the area of weaponry. Several examples could be cited, but one of the most extraordinary involves the United States B-29 Superfortress long-range bomber. Toward the end of World War II, three of these aircraft became crippled and had to divert to Vladivostok in Siberia. They were captured by the Russians and "dissected . . . 'rivet by rivet,' making exact copies of the 105,000 parts, which they used to create . . . the Tu-4 'Bull.'"[10] This Russian bomber looked very similar and performed almost identically to the B-29. In fact, the Russians did such a good job of reverse-engineering the Superfortress, their Tu-4 bomber's engines tended to overheat and catch fire, just like the American version.[11] Such is one of the dangers inherent in any reverse engineering project. See Figure 7–1.

Even today, reverse engineering is still popular in the military realm,[12] but now it has also become big business in the arenas of computer science and microbiology. Both of these fast-growing areas must deal with incredibly complex systems whose operations may not be well-understood or well-documented. Hence, reverse engineering approaches are being applied to organize and explore these complexities. Although computer science involves human-made complexities and microbiology involves those that arise in nature, the tools of reverse engineering have proved extremely valuable to both fields. In his book, *Reverse Engineering: TecŪology of Reinvention*, technology expert Wego Wang writes, "The human body is a beautiful piece of engineering work in nature. Reverse engineering is the most effective way to reinvent the component parts of this engineering marvel due to lack of the original design data."[13]

Furthermore, design theorist William Dembski promotes reverse engineering of natural systems as a primary emphasis of the Intelligent Design (ID) movement. In his seminal book, *Intelligent*

Figure 7–1   The B-29 Superfortress suffered from a design flaw in which its engines might overheat and catch fire.
© Keith Tarrier/Shutterstock.com

Design: The Bridge between Science and Theology he writes, "Intelligent design's positive contribution to science is to reverse engineer objects shown to be designed. Indeed the design theorist is a reverse engineer. Unconstrained by naturalism, the design theorist finds plenty of natural objects attributable to design (this is especially true for biological systems). Having determined that certain natural objects are designed, the design theorist next investigates how they were produced. Yet because evidence of how they were produced is typically incomplete (at least for natural objects), the design theorist is left instead with investigating how these could have been produced. This is reverse engineering."[14] In the minds of many scientists, the ID movement delegitimizes itself by exceeding the boundaries of science. This obviously depends on how one defines science. But the big questions in life require more than what science can bring to the table anyway. So why not encourage science and philosophy (and other disciplines) to play nicely together. There are already some indications that such inter-disciplinary efforts are yielding answers that many are finding very satisfying. The next section will focus on the thinking behind the reverse engineering approach.

Philosophy of Affordance-Based Reverse Engineering

As discussed in a previous chapter, making sense of the universe will require experts from many different fields of study to "put their heads together." And engineers should certainly be in the mix. In fact, according to engineer and origin-of-life researcher Bryant Shiller, "An engineering background affords some distinct advantages . . . engineers are often called upon to combine the findings of a number of diverse scientific disciplines in order to arrive at practical solutions and to achieve specific goals. This is the traditional application of engineering principles. But those same principles are eminently suitable for the study of systems already in operation. It's called 'reverse engineering.' The quest for the solution to the puzzle of how and/or why life came to be on the planet Earth can benefit from this kind of mentality—the engineering mentality."[15] If the universe is engineered for life, then an affordance-based reverse engineering analysis should assist in confirming this reality, and also help in answering further questions.

Affordance-based reverse engineering is simply a reverse engineering approach that focuses on the affordances that are inherent in the system. Recall that affordances can be nested, and can exhibit quality (degree to which they afford something) and polarity (considered positive or negative). Since affordances arise out of relationships between the elements of a system, a straightforward approach entails listing all the elements of the system and then identifying and classifying the resulting affordances. Of course, this assumes that our accumulated, but limited, store of human knowledge and experiences is sufficient for the task. It may well be that systems as complicated as the universe or even life on Earth can only be partially analyzed in this way at this point in the history of humanity. An important part of an accurate and honest analysis is an admission of that which is not yet well-understood, or even known.

However, several important questions can be addressed through affordance-based reverse engineering: How does the system work? What does it afford to the end-user? What are the part-to-part affordances? When did the system come into existence? How did the system come into existence? What are the qualities of the part-to-part and end-user affordances? Has the system experienced degradation or enhancement over time, and how has this affected its affordances? What is the balance of positive to negative affordances? Do the positives outweigh the negatives? Do the affordances provide a legitimate indication of meaning and purpose? Why is there life in the universe? Why is there anything at all? These questions can only be answered from the realm of human experience; a limited and finite reference point. Even so, our ability to discover real truths about the cosmos and make use of these truths to engineer solutions to problems (and answers to important questions) gives us real hope in the face of such daunting challenges.

In an effort to cut through some of the complexity and organize the elements and affordances of any system, engineering researcher Johnathan Maier has recently proposed a graphical tool called the affordance structure matrix (ASM). It is a two-dimensional array with the elements of the system listed across the top, and the resulting affordances listed down the left side, with boxes filled in with plus or minus signs (polarity) to indicate which elements contribute to each affordance. According to Maier, the ASM "is a helpful tool that has been developed that allows designers to compare designs by assessing the quality of individual affordances."[16] He also claims that a systematic evaluation of the affordances of each part of the system can be combined into a comprehensive ASM, including both part-to-part and end-user affordances. The system is then effectively reverse-engineered in the sense that its operation is well understood.[17] Maier's graphical approach to handling the complexity of reverse engineering projects is a recent positive contribution in the area of design science, and is continuing to be refined.

One of the limitations of Maier's approach when applied to natural systems is its apparent preference for static and complete systems; those that are already in a finished and unchanging state. Many systems found in nature, especially living organisms, seem to still be "in process" and have a very dynamic history. They have changed, or evolved, over time, according to multiple streams of converging evidence from the natural sciences. And this is part of the reason why sequentially nested affordances may not be easily captured by the ASM. It is therefore proposed that multiple layers of affordance structure matrices (ASMs) may help to illuminate the full history of any naturally occurring system. The following example, in which this approach is applied to living organisms, may help to clarify this proposal.

Affordance-Based Reverse Engineering in Systems Biology

All living organisms make use of the informational structure of the DNA molecule as they are guided toward maturity. However, this structure works in concert with many other structures and mechanisms common to life. These life-supporting structures exhibit many part-to-part affordances, but they also may have precursor, or preexisting, structures through which they developed or from which they emerged. Furthermore, a complete analysis of living organisms should not consider the creature in isolation from its life-sustaining environment. This symbiosis between organism and habitat, and the evolution of that habitat, must also be taken into account in any affordance-based reverse engineering analysis. We still have much to learn about the history of life on Earth and how it could have originated. But the scientific evidence seems to point clearly to a story with a recurring theme of how one thing led to another (or afforded another) over and over again. This is a story of nested affordances.

Consider even the simplest single-celled living organism along with its environment. The complexity represented by this system is already at a level that would severely challenge the construction of a complete ASM. But even if all the elements of the system could be listed along with all of their affordance-producing interactions, the whole story of this organism's existence has not yet been told. Yes, one may develop a relatively good understanding of how it works, but what about the other questions (listed earlier) that beg to be answered? I propose that a step in the direction of answering those questions is achieved by considering the underlying nested affordances that play multiple roles in the emergence of this organism.

Without getting too deep into the details, we know that the biological structures that make up a living cell are afforded by biomolecules that combine because of certain chemical affinities, or electrical attractions. Likewise, biomolecules are afforded by the linking up of chemical elements such as carbon, hydrogen, oxygen, and nitrogen. These, as with all the atoms of our periodic table of elements, are afforded by the hellish conditions that persist inside those huge balls of fire that twinkle for us in the dark night sky. Likewise, the chemically creative action of stars is afforded by a balance between the inward pull of gravity and the outward thermodynamic push of such an intense combustion. The eventual explosion of stars—or supernova—and coalescence into new generations of stars affords the heavier chemical elements. The fact that stars even exist at all is afforded by the fundamental forces of physics and the initial conditions of the matter and energy that make up this universe.

Ultimately, one could say that the laws of physics, chemistry, and biology play an important role in affording life to organisms. But natural laws are somewhat nebulous, not being physical entities, and may not be appropriate to carry the necessary weight in the story of affordances. Even so, philosopher Richard Swinburne astutely asks why we have these particular laws of nature, and not some others.[18] It appears to be because of the life-friendly consequences they afford. Although an effective means of organizing and illustrating this state-of-affairs is still being developed, this entire set of nested affordances could be laid out in a series of ASMs which represent various stages of the system and its precursors over time, as well as the ancestral connections between them. It should be clear at this point that the entire universe has been caught up in the story of life on earth.

Extending the Reverse Engineering Mindset to All of Nature

Recall that science involves observation and experimentation in an effort to gain knowledge of the cosmos. As such, it is limited in the types of evidence and questions it can address on its own;

namely, those pertaining to the natural world. The reigning paradigm within science today is called methodological naturalism. This scheme entails that a scientist adopt the working presupposition that "nature is all that exists" while practicing the methods of science, even if the scientist actually believes in the existence of God. On the one hand, this makes sense because one should not be entertaining the possibility of a miraculous event occurring during a supposedly repeatable scientific experiment. But on the other hand, if God does exist, it would be reasonable to assume that nature provides evidence for this, just as Judeo-Christianity claims. So to address the bigger questions of the cosmos with disregard for the Maker and the Maker's purposes seems shortsighted.

Some researchers have suggested a kind of compromise. Although the scientific method remains difficult to accurately and comprehensively define, it may be divided into three stages: testing and data-collection, data-interpretation, and theory-building. Science also relies on the Principle of Objectivity which states, "the only objects or processes that can be properly studied by the scientific method are those that have an empirical, objective reality (because they are the only ones that can be accurately measured)."[19] And God is not a tangible, observable entity that can be measured and studied in the lab.

However, philosopher Michael Corey argues that God can be a part of the modern scientific method without being involved in every aspect. Science should remain objective, and God can be considered as the primary cause for the things we observe without jeopardizing the Principle of Objectivity. God makes use of "secondary causation" by creating things that continue to carry out processes on their own following the laws of physics to bring about what we presently observe. Thus explicit metaphysical considerations may be excluded during testing and data-collection, but welcomed (for good reasons) during data-interpretation and theory-building.[20]

For the case of living organisms described earlier, experiments and observations have identified an extensive and complex system of nested affordances. Recall that affordances are simply statements of what can occur due to the relationships between elements of a system. As such, they do not necessarily imply intentionality or purpose behind the system; they are metaphysically neutral. But when an abundance of affordances are strung together in a dependent sequential (nested) fashion, the data suggests a particular interpretation involving the influence of an engineer. At which point a theory may be formed and further tested; namely that life and the universe itself are engineered systems.

Although Corey would claim that we are still doing science at this point since the supernatural element was only introduced during the data interpretation and theory building stages, others would vehemently disagree. But does it really matter when considering the bigger picture? Trying to determine exactly what constitutes science, and what does not, is known as the demarcation problem. And getting caught up in this problem only diverts us from focusing on life's important questions. Another alternative is to allow science to maintain its stricter boundaries, and simply recognize that reverse engineering studies that ask deeper questions will necessarily draw from fields of knowledge and experience outside of science, including philosophy and theology.

The Coherence of an Engineered Universe

Living systems possess an extraordinary set of nested affordances within themselves, but their local habitats and larger cosmic environment also contribute to additional nested affordances that reach back all the way to the beginnings of matter, energy, space, and time. In this sense, the universe exhibits an amazing interconnectedness. John Muir, naturalist and founder of the Sierra Club, recognized this in 1911 when he wrote, "When we try to pick out anything by itself, we find it hitched to everything else in the universe."[21] Theoretical physicist and bestselling author Lisa Randall agrees in her most recent book where she describes "a Universe in which the small and the large, the visible and the hidden are intimately related."[22]

We have already seen how the chemical elements manufactured within stars ultimately afford the appropriate constituents for the emergence of living organisms. But these same elements, along with a few others, ultimately end up affording a livable and symbiotic environment as well. Planet Earth and its history is also a story of nested affordances. Many of these details are described in *The Privileged Planet* by Guillermo Gonzalez and Jay Richards.[23] They emphasize that the same features of the cosmos that afford life and habitat, also afford scientific discovery about origins, and the engineered nature of our existence. The universe appears to be laid out specifically to afford knowledge of its nested affordances to those advanced life forms who are curious enough to investigate.

Planet Earth affords life to a huge diversity of organisms over vast stretches of time. The Earth's relationships to various parts of our solar system facilitate this advantageous situation. The sun affords a life-sustaining level of radiant energy. The powerful gravitational fields of large planets like Jupiter and Saturn attract asteroids and meteors, affording a relatively peaceful surface dwelling on Earth. Our large single moon affords important tidal motions and a stable spin axis for the Earth, which affords a relatively even climate. The moon was afforded by a collision that occurred between the early Earth and a somewhat smaller object. This collision also afforded a thin, transparent atmosphere that is conducive to advanced life.

Our Milky Way galaxy affords an environment where enough of the necessary heavier chemical elements (which are needed for life) could coalesce into our solar system and planet. The galaxy simultaneously affords a relatively safe place for the Earth to hang out between two of its spiral arms. The spiral structure of our galaxy is afforded by a combination of dark energy, centrifugal forces, and gravitational forces that work in concert to maintain its shape over a vast stretch of time. The balance of dark energy and gravity afforded an expansion rate for the early universe that was precisely what was needed to sustain the system of stars, galaxies, and other celestial objects that make up our cosmos.

The order, harmony, and value that results from these nested affordances is typical of engineered systems, and not typical of random, chaotic, or accidentally-thrown-together systems. Admittedly, one interpretation of this evidence is that we are simply fortunate recipients of a long string of advantageous coincidences. Furthermore, living organisms tend to adapt to their environment, giving the appearance of the environment being just right for them. While this is true, it doesn't seem, at least to this engineer, to go nearly far enough in explaining our wonderfully gifted circumstances. Indeed, the adaptability of living organisms fits nicely as another engineered feature that affords the sustenance of life; not something that we would expect to arise out of an accidental situation. From an engineering perspective, reality reeks of intentionality.

Just after Christmas of 2015, the writers of the comic strip *Baby Blues*, Rick Kirkman and Jerry Scott, provided a humorous and easy-to-understand illustration of affordance-based reverse engineering in the comic shown in Figure 7–2.[24] Hammie is not caught in the act of stealing the last of the Christmas fudge by his mom, but rather, she reverse-engineers the truth by recognizing the obvious implications of nested affordances. She knows that her fudge provides the end-user affordance of

Figure 7–2   Hammie Helps to Illustrate How Evidence Can Point to Purposeful Events
Baby Blues © 2016 Baby Blues Partnership, Dist. by King Features Syndicate, Inc.

delicious, mouth-watering satisfaction, in this case to Hammie, but its location on the top shelf of the cupboard presents the negative (to Hammie) affordance of "out-of-reach-ness." That's why she put them there! Some researchers call such negative affordances "anti-affordances."

Assuming that she observed a chair in an out-of-place location next to the counter under the cupboard, and a stack of books, also in an out-of-place location, on the counter below the cupboard, she probably conducted affordance-based reverse engineering. Without really thinking about all these details, she quickly made an inference-to-the-best-explanation based on the observation of the following nested affordances. For Hammie, the chair affords access to the counter. Having won the counter, a high enough stack of books affords access to the top shelf of the cupboard. Notice how the second affordance is dependent on the previous affordance. The books do not afford access to the fudge unless the chair is deployed first, hence the nestedness. Of course, the corroborating evidence of fudgy hand-prints also played a part in implicating poor Hammie. Also notice how his claim that it was all an accident "rings hollow" in the face of such strong evidence against him. Humans know, almost instinctively, that nested affordances which result in value tend to imply intentionality and at least some level of engineering expertise.

RECONSTRUCTING THE MAKER FROM THE THINGS HE HAS MADE

On the day David came home from the Marines, my sister Lilly (two years my elder) and I were standing in our breezeway looking out the front windows for him. The breezeway made for a very interesting entrance into our home. It was a small room with a stone fireplace and a gun cabinet on one side, and a large detailed National Geographic map of the world on the opposite wall. I was fascinated with maps as a child, and Lilly and I enjoyed playing the "map game" in our breezeway, where we would alternately quiz each other on the exact locations of various obscure cities, rivers, or mountain ranges across the globe. Lilly was very difficult to stump, and I sometime studied the map in her absence in an effort to find the "most obscure point in the world." Much to my delight, I later discovered that we were rewarded for such knowledge in fifth grade geography class, and my poor teacher, Mrs. McDowell, had a hard time keeping up.

All of a sudden we received an update. "David's home! But he's gone back to say hello to the grandparents first." However, Lilly and I couldn't wait, so we took off out the back door at a flat-out sprint. My mom's mom, Grandma McCarthy, lived in a trailer about fifty yards behind our house. And my dad's parents lived in a "double-wide" about fifty yards further back. My very earliest clear memory is one of many visits Lilly and I made to our grandparents. The thing that made that earliest memory stand out is also the thing that serves as a time stamp for that early visit to this very day. For some strange reason (the kind of thing known only to small children), we were playing a game where I would tickle my sister whenever she would say what year it was. That's how I remember that it was 1965. She kept saying it, so I just kept tickling her. I was either two or three years old at the time. I also remember that our grandparents always had a treat ready to give us; a chocolate chip cookie, a bag of corn chips, or a hard roll with butter. Sometimes Grandma Halsmer played a simple card game with me called "War." And if I erroneously tried to grab a "trick" that she had won, she'd say in that sweet old voice, "Ah ah! Don't burn your fingers."

But now I was a few years older, and we were running back toward the grandparents to see David, whom we hadn't seen in three years. As I described at the beginning of this chapter, his reputation preceded him, largely because of the things he had made before he left for the Marines. We ran into him on the sidewalk outside of Grandma McCarthy's place. He was still wearing his uniform and his crewcut. I remember thinking that his hair (or lack thereof) looked really funny. But we squealed as we hugged him as hard as we could. Homecomings are one of life's great joys.

Over the next few weeks and months, the time we got to spend with David only served to confirm our fond memories of him. He would soon be on his way to building and flying his own powered hang-glider with, of course, a video camera strapped to the wing (not too shabby for the 1970s). It occurs to me that a similar situation seems to exist with the realm of nature. Just as the things David had made "spoke" to us of his character and personality in his absence, so too, the creation speaks of God's existence and excellence of character.

Like a great chess player who is able to "see" several moves deep into a game,[25] God's great engineering expertise is demonstrated by the complex array of nested affordances scientists have uncovered in nature. Perhaps God is the kind of being who is able to see from the beginning, all the way to the end of this universe he has made. That would not be surprising, given the magnificence of forethought displayed by his creation.

STUDY QUESTIONS

1. Describe a period of time when you were separated from a loved one. How did you keep the relationship alive?
2. Why might methodological naturalism be appropriately applied to some phases of science, but not others? Which phases might be best conducted free of such restrictions?
3. What can we learn from one of the earliest known examples of reverse engineering?
4. What did reverse engineering studies teach Leonardo da Vinci about the human body?

5. What is one inherent danger in reverse engineering, especially when copying a technology with great accuracy?

6. Why should an engineering background be advantageous for reasoning about the universe?

7. How would you answer the series of questions addressed by affordance-based reverse engineering for the system of life on earth?

8. Sketch a simple Affordance Structure Matrix for an electric hair dryer. Attempt the same exercise for a creek that has been dammed by a beaver.

9. Discuss the limitations of the Affordance Structure Matrix. How might it be expanded to better accommodate natural systems with nested affordances?

10. How do the initial conditions of the universe, the fundamental forces of physics, and the laws of nature all contribute to the emergence of living systems?

11. How can thinking about God be part of the modern scientific method without sacrificing the Principle of Objectivity?

12. Do you think intentionality and ingenuity can be explained away by luck or the adaptability of evolving systems? Why or why not?

13. Describe a time when you were reunited with a loved one after spending time apart. Were there any positive affordances that resulted?

ENDNOTES

1. One of my favorite original poems concerns playing with army men, growing up, and the horror of war:

Lost Army Men
I had a box of army men.
I don't know where they are.
Their arms and legs are rigid.
So they can't have gotten far.
Little brother must have found them
And has kept them for his own.
Or maybe I misplaced them,
Or I gave them out on loan.
Maybe my elders took them
when advised by some wise sage,
"He really shouldn't play with them
at his unchildish age!"
I must confess, I made the sounds
of battle as I played.
Ignorant of the living hell
when real war is made.
I had a box of army men
from Weber's Hobby Store.

They were only made of plastic.
So they can't have gone to war.
I know they are long gone.
And where they've gone, I cannot say.
I've heard that some old soldiers
never die; just fade away.
I must grow up and face the fact
that army men are dumb.
At least until our grandkids come
And we can play with some!

2. Some years later I constructed a poem to commemorate this occasion when I "hit the jackpot":

Found Army Men
There is no greater joy to a boy of ten
Than to find an old box full of army men
So skillfully painted and packed in cotton
Tucked up in the rafters and long forgotten
I could hardly believe my peepers!
Finders-keepers, losers-weepers.

3. Thomas Jay Oord, *Defining Love: A Philosophical, Scientific and Theological Engagement* (Grand Rapids, MI: Brazos Press, 2010), 15.

4. Laboratory sciences typically abide by methodological naturalism, rightly restricting considering to "natural" causes, but overarching questions, such as those that arise in cosmology and its philosophical implications, may be best addressed by the freedom of thought that results from loosening such restrictions.

5. Robert W. Messler, Jr., *Reverse Engineering: Mechanisms, Structures, Systems and Materials* (New York: McGraw-Hill, 2014), xv.

6. Ian Tattersall and Jeffrey Schwartz, "Evolution of the Genus *Homo*," *Annual Review of Earth and Planetary Sciences* 37 (May 2009): 81.

7. Messler, *Reverse Engineering*, 29–32.

8. Messler, *Reverse Engineering*, 9–11.

9. Messler, *Reverse Engineering*, 10–12.

10. Messler, *Reverse Engineering*, 44.

11. http://www.rb-29.net/html/03relatedstories/03.03shortstories/03.03.10contss.htm.

12. https://www.rt.com/news/205267-iran-replica-us-drone/.

13. Wego Wang, *Reverse Engineering: TecÚology of Reinvention* (Boca Raton, FL: CRC Press, 2011): 6.

14. William Dembski, *Intelligent Design: The Bridge between Science and Theology* (Downers Grove, IL: InterVarsity, 1999), 108–109.

15. Bryant M. Shiller, *Origin of Life: The 5th Option* (Victoria, BC: Trafford, 2004): xiii.

16. Jonathan Maier, *Affordance Based Design: Theoretical Foundations and Practical Applications* (Saarbrucken, Germany: VDM Verlag, 2011), 21. As a simple example of an ASM (Affordance Structure Matrix), Maier presents the following breakdown of a robotic vacuum cleaner from Jonathan R. A. Maier, "Rethinking Design Theory," *Mechanical Engineering* (ASME, September 2008): 36.

▼ Affordance structure matrix for a robotic vacuum cleaner.

		handles	static sensor	battery	propulsion motors	self charger unit	vacuum motor	air filter	wheels	brush	anti-skid padding	debris bin	belt	power button	computer	impeller assembly	TOTAL
+AUA	maneuverability			X	X				X		X				X		5
+AUA	aesthetics	X				X								X			3
-AUA	electric shock		X	X	X	X	X		X	X				X	X		9
-AUA	noise				X		X	X	X		X					X	6
+AAA	ability to reach various surfaces				X				X						X		3
+AAA	suction capability			X			X	X		X		X	X		X	X	8
-AAA	clogging						X	X		X		X	X		X	X	7
-AAA	power consumption			X	X	X	X	X	X	X				X	X	X	10
	TOTAL	1	1	4	5	3	5	4	5	4	2	2	2	3	6	4	51

17. J. R. A. Maier, T. Ezhilan, and G. M. Fadel, "The Affordance Structure Matrix—A Concept Exploration and Attention Directing Tool for Affordance Based Design," Proceedings of the ASME International Design Engineering Technical Conferences and Information in Engineering Conference, Las Vegas, NV, Paper no. DETC2007-34526, 2003.

18. Richard Swinburne, *The Existence of God*, 2nd ed. (Oxford: Oxford University Press, 2004), 172.

19. Michael Corey, *The God Hypothesis: Discovering Design in our "Just Right" Goldilocks Universe* (Lanham, MD: Rowman & Littlefield, 2007), 268.

20. Corey, *God Hypothesis*, 269.

21. John Muir, *My First Summer in the Sierra* (Boston: Houghton Mifflin, 1911), 110.

22. Lisa Randall, *Dark Matter and the Dinosaurs: The Astounding Interconnectedness of the Universe* (New York: HarperCollins, 2015), front matter.

23. Guillermo Gonzalez and Jay W. Richards, *The Privileged Planet: How Our Place in the Cosmos is Designed for Discovery* (Washington, DC: Regnery, 2004).

24. Rick Kirkman and Jerry Scott, *Baby Blues* comic strip, December 29, 2015.

25. In fact, the game of chess offers another example of nested affordances, since each move affords the further unfolding of a strategic plan. Advancing a central pawn affords avenues of mobility for the queen and bishops, while also affording control of the center of the board. Developing pieces to advantageous squares affords attacking opportunities, while also affording the ability to castle, which afford protection for the king, etc.

CHAPTER EIGHT

The "Big Picture" of Design and Reverse Engineering

CHARACTER ENGINEERING AT ST. BONIFACE ELEMENTARY SCHOOL

The "big picture" of design can be illustrated by the way my parents so trustingly enlisted the help of the Lafayette Catholic School System in engineering me into the fine specimen of humanity that I exemplify to this day. Seriously though, I was very rough around the edges as a school-aged kid, and vestiges of my social ineptitude have stubbornly persisted into adulthood. But growing up in a large family did serve to ease the transition to institutionalized education at St. Boniface Elementary School. We lived a good five miles out of town, so we had to catch a school bus in both directions to take advantage of this early opportunity to better ourselves.

On cold winter mornings I used to sit, looking out the side window of our house while it was still dark, watching for the distinct orange and yellow running lights of the bus, so as not to be caught by surprise. That had happened a few times before, and inevitably, as I streaked out the front door and across our long front yard with lunch and books and papers in hand, I always seemed to forget about the slight dip in our lawn about two-thirds of the way out to the street. This resulted in quite a show for the students watching my progress out the bus windows, as I suddenly sensed the ground recede from beneath my feet while my legs windmilled away at maximum rpm. As you can imagine, there is only one outcome to this unfortunate predicament, and it forever stained my reputation with the bus-riding community. Gravity took its toll, which turned out to be more than I could pay, as my whirling feet reconnected with the ground in altogether strange and unpredictable locations. Lunch, books, and papers went flying in all directions as I executed a spectacular head-over-heels tumbling sequence of which Olympic gymnast coach Bela Karolyi would not have been proud. The kindly bus driver waited patiently as I picked myself up and tried to track down all my things. My fellow students were not so kind. Such was my dubious start at elementary education.

I am extremely grateful, however, for the various teachers, coaches, and counselors who invested in me at this tender age. My first grade teacher, Sister Roberta, was so sweet and kind that if she ever had to leave the room for a few moments, I would immediately burst into tears. I eventually grew accustomed to being away from home, and even discovered some enjoyable activities with which I was very familiar. Being from Indiana, I soon learned that the sport of basketball had attained something of a sacred status among the schools in our town. And the St. Boniface Panthers were expected to "pick-and-roll" their way past the likes of the St. Lawrence Ramblers and the St. Mary's Yellow Jackets. Fortunately, I had some previous experience shooting baskets on the hoop above our driveway at home. But I was about to experience a basketball baptism of fire.

Our elementary-level basketball coach was Bob Metzger, a drill sergeant type of character who would make us run sprints, or laps around the gym, at the drop of a hat. He would have us jump up and touch a spot on the wall, over and over again until our calf muscles began to cramp up. He would make us wear special goggles with the bottom half of the lenses taped over, to help us learn how to dribble the ball without looking at it. In many ways, he pushed us beyond our erroneously self-imposed limitations into unanticipated accomplishments. Even just a few years out of elementary school, I remember thinking how thankful I was to have a coach who motivated me to do things I didn't think I could do. Bob Metzger is probably one of the biggest reasons I still enjoy competitive running and basketball so much today.

When I think back on my elementary school days, all the adversity I experienced served to build my character. In this sense, adversity, in a positive relational environment, affords character formation. My parents had a good relationship with St. Boniface Catholic Church, so they entrusted the engineering of my character and education to them. The nuns and other teachers employed by the church sometimes had an adversarial relationship with us students, but they patiently and skillfully drew us on to academic excellence. I must admit that often it was painful,[1] but I had a good relationship with my parents, so I trusted them in making these decisions. From these examples, it should be clear that relationships are important, not only in the engineering of a child's character, but in any engineering endeavor where multiple parties are involved. Let's take a closer look at the relationships within the big picture of engineering product design and reverse engineering.

The Big Picture of Engineering Design

The engineering of any original artifact or product inevitably involves some adversity. These difficulties can be minimized by tending to the relationships between the three main entities in the big picture of engineering product design:

1. The engineer or designer, who designs and oversees the building of the product.
2. The product, or artifact, that is engineered.
3. The customer, or end user, of the product.

(See Figure 8–1 following.)[2]

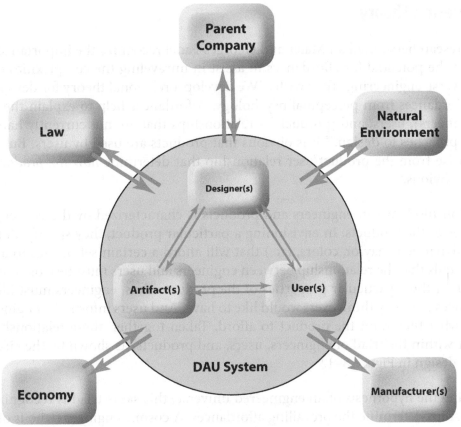

Figure 8–1   The Big Picture of Engineering Product Design[15]
© Kendall Hunt Publishing Company

Other factors such as the policies of the parent company, any potential impact on the environ-ment, the availability of manufacturers, the current state of the economy, and any pertinent legal issues should also be considered. But the triad of engineer, product, and user, and the relationships between these three entities, are the primary considerations in any engineering project.

To be successful, the engineer should understand something of the needs, desires, lifestyle, and resources of the typical end user who will employ the product. In producing smartphones, for exam-ple, engineers know that customers desire a multitude of capabilities (affordances) that can be quickly and easily accessed. This requires that the smartphone be engineered in a way that readily establishes a good relationship between phone and user. Using the phone for various purposes should not only be convenient, but fun and easy, without too long of a learning curve or too much complexity for the average user to endure. Finally, the relationship between the engineer and the phone is character-ized by intimate knowledge of the fundamental scientific and engineering principles to permit the profitable production of such a desirable piece of technology. Thus it becomes clear that these three relationships are critically important for successful engineering.

Relational Design Theory

Engineering researchers Jonathan Maier and Georges Fadel recognize the importance of these relationships, and the potential for affordances to assist in unraveling the complexities of engineering design and reverse engineering. They write, "We develop a relational theory for design based on the concept of affordances from perceptual psychology. Affordances help to explain the entanglement between [engineers], users, and [products]—relationships that are not currently handled by function based approaches to design."[3] It is obvious that products are used by users. But it is the affordances that arise from the product/user relationship that determine *how the product can be used*. This is not so obvious.[4]

The relationship between engineers and products is characterized by the way engineers create the affordances of the products. In envisioning a particular product, they specify all the properties (geometries, dynamic behavior, colors, etc.) that will afford a certain set of uses to a certain set of users.[5] This entails that the relationship between engineers and users must be close enough to afford the realization of these particular properties of the product. Thus, engineers must identify a target set of affordances that they think users would like to have. And users inform the engineers of desired uses; that is, what they want the product to afford. Taken together, these relationships define the entanglement within the triad of engineers, users, and products, as shown by the circularity in the big picture of design in Figure 8–1.[6]

In exploring the hypothesis of an engineered universe, this same triad is recognized, and these same relationships determine the prevailing affordances. A cosmic engineer (who is often identified as God), or "cosmineer" is proposed as one or more entities who envisions, creates, and sustains the entire cosmos. So in this sense, a generic understanding of God serves as the "engineer" of the triad. Thus, the "product" could be the universe itself or elements of the universe that invite further study, such as planet Earth. Identification of the "user" depends somewhat on the choice of product. If Earth is chosen for study, then humans and animals could be considered legitimate users of this product. If the entire universe is chosen, then, again, mankind may be considered as a user, even though humanity is also part of the universe. But multiple theistic traditions also recognize the sense in which God is the ultimate end user of the cosmos, since it was made to accomplish divine purposes.

A further and more interesting dynamic arises when considering the fact that humans are late-comers on the scene. We are born into this world as truth-seekers and truth-soakers. We have a seemingly insatiable desire for truth and we continually soak up an enormous amount of data, even from infancy. Our desire to understand reality flows from a realization that such understanding affords so many valuable things. Our very lives daily depend on an accurate understanding of the world; things like, "I need air to breathe" and "I should avoid falling more than a few feet." This puts us in the position of being an explorer or investigator of our world. If the universe is indeed an engineered system, then the technical term for this position is "reverse engineer." Now it is helpful to expand the triad representing the big picture of design to include this new fourth entity: the investigator, or reverse engineer.

The Big Picture of Reverse Engineering

In general then, any reverse engineering project involves interesting relationships between four entities:

1. The original engineer of the product.
2. The product itself.
3. The original or current user of the product
4. The current investigator of the product, or reverse engineer.[7]

Figure 8–2 illustrates this situation below, where Maier's big picture of engineering design has been modified to include a central position for the investigator.

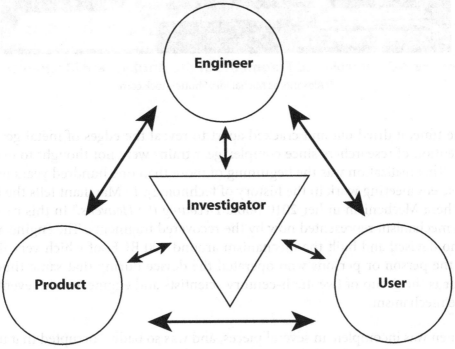

Figure 8–2 The Big Picture of Reverse Engineering[15]
Source: Dominic Halsmer

Double arrows between all four entities emphasize that there are now twice as many relationships to attend to (six instead of three) in order to fully understand the circumstances associated with the investigation of a particular product.

As a simple example, consider the case of the Antikythera Mechanism. Around the beginning of the twentieth century, a major archaeological find was made in the discovery of the contents of an undersea shipwreck off the coast of the Greek island of Antikythera. Many valuable artifacts were recovered from the wreck, which was dated to about 100 BCE. In addition to beautiful marble statues and ancient artifacts, a curious, corroded, and coral-encrusted block (and related pieces) of an unknown nature was retrieved and placed in the basement of the Athens Museum (see Figure 8–3 following).

Figure 8–3   Recovered Fragments of the Antikythera Mechanism[8]
© Alexandros Michailidis/Shutterstock.com

After some time, it dried out and cracked apart to reveal the edges of metal gear wheels. This caught the attention of researchers since complex gear trains were not thought to exist at any time near 100 BCE. This realization was the beginning of more than one hundred years of the most fascinating reverse engineering work in the history of technology. Jo Marchant tells the intriguing tale of the Antikythera Mechanism in her 2010 book, *Decoding the Heavens*.[9] In this case, the product is the original mechanism represented now by the recovered fragments. The engineer is the person or persons who devised and built the mechanism around 100 BCE, of which very little is known. The user was the person or persons who operated the device during that same time period. And the investigator is the group of twentieth-century scientists and engineers who eventually reverse-engineered the mechanism.

The specimen was incomplete in several pieces, and was so badly corrupted that initial attempts at reverse engineering were very discouraging. However, with painstaking effort over a period of about one hundred years, the corruption produced by two millennia of seawater was teased apart from the original engineering that went into the device. With the help of advanced measurement systems like x-rays and sonograms, functioning replicas were eventually produced by multiple investigators. They were able to identify the parts of the mechanism (including twenty-eight different gears) and how those parts interacted (providing part-to-part affordances) in delivering affordances to an end user.

Marchant provides the following insight, "Scrutinizing the details of the gearwheels and inscriptions, however, wasn't the only way to investigate the mechanism . . . archaeologists also studied the rest of the salvaged cargo [and culture of the time]. Their discoveries help to paint a vivid picture of when the ship sailed, where her load was being taken, and the sort of world from which she came. From there, we can guess at the origins of the Antikythera Mechanism itself and how it ended up on its final journey."[10] Ultimately, it was recognized that the mechanism affords a mechanical simulation of the motion of the moon and planets including the prediction of eclipses. In effect, it is believed to be one of the first analog computers, about a thousand years earlier than was ever thought possible.

There are a few things to be gleaned from this classic example of reverse engineering of a man-made system, and perhaps applied to natural systems. The quality of engineering and workmanship reflects on the original engineer. Marchant records how carefully engraved letters in the outer casing of the mechanism indicate the work of a "master craftsman," rather than an "unskilled laborer." Information about origin and destiny may also be uncovered by expanding the investigation beyond just dissection and measurement of the specimen. Relationships between potential users of such a mechanism and those ingenious enough to engineer it were investigated. The history and culture of the time, in addition to the other artifacts with which it was found, helped to unravel the mystery of its origin and purpose. This is the nature of reverse engineering projects: all possible information that could be pertinent in recovering original design information is considered.

Relationships in the Big Picture of Reverse Engineering

In comparison to the big picture of design, the new relationships to be explored in the big picture of reverse engineering are those between the investigator and the other three entities (product, engineer, and user). The investigator must be drawn to the product somehow. What is it about the product that attracts the attention and efforts of the investigator? How does the product afford wonder and curiosity? It must be beautiful or complex in a way that merits further study, or promises benefits to the investigator upon successful completion of the reverse engineering project.

Of course, the easiest way to make progress in reverse engineering is for the investigator to communicate with the original engineer. Then all questions could be answered directly from the source of the product. But this was not possible in the case of the Antikythera Mechanism, since its remnants were discovered and analyzed about 2,000 years after it was built. In cases where the original engineer is unavailable, investigators will sometimes attempt to recover documentation, owner's manuals, or any written reference that might lend insight into the engineering of the product. A conscientious and thorough engineer might anticipate this eventuality, and take measures to ensure that a product is well documented or self-explanatory. This is especially true if part of the purpose of the product is to reveal something of the power and glory of the original engineer. This is exactly the case in some theistic traditions where the entire realm of nature is taken as product. According to Romans 1:20, nature affords (limited) knowledge of God.

Finally, the relationship between the investigator and the user can lead to some significant insights. What are the positive affordances enjoyed by the user, and negative affordances endured by the user, of a particular product? In some cases, an investigator serves to mediate feedback from the user to the engineer on how to improve the product. This highlights the possibility of re-engineering or redesign (refining a design based on information from users), which often accompanies reverse engineering projects. Maier and Fadel also propose "an affordance-based method for reverse engineering and redesign"[11] in situations where a "product already exists and is being analyzed to see how it works and could possibly be improved."[12]

In describing this process, Meyer and Fadel write, "The information gleaned through a systematic evaluation of the affordances of each part of the product can be conglomerated into a complete detail level affordance structure, including affordances between the product and potential users, and affordances between the parts themselves."[13] They go on to conclude, "After the creation of such a detailed affordance structure, the product has been effectively reverse-engineered in the sense that its operation should be well understood."[14] Figure 8–4 shown below illustrates an affordance structure for a passenger automobile.

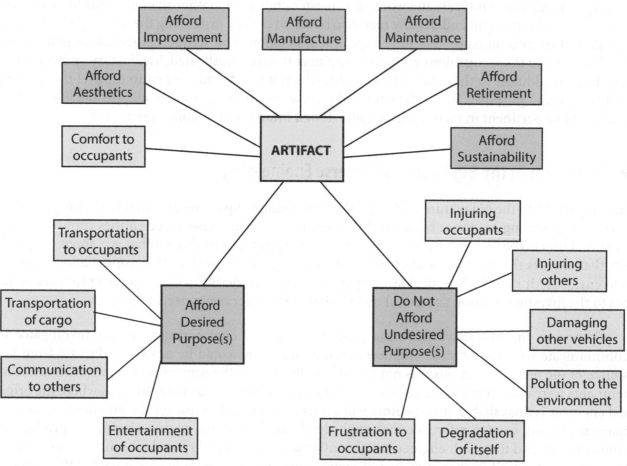

Figure 8–4   Affordance Structure for a Passenger Automobile[15]
©Kendall Hunt Publishing Company

The affordance structure shown in Figure 8–4 is only a summary of the end user affordances for an automobile and does not include the detailed part-to-part affordances that exist for the many subsystems of such a product. A complete affordance structure with all the details would take many pages, perhaps volumes, to illustrate. Even so, this type of affordance-based analysis has proven useful for engineering product design, reverse engineering, and redesign.

How Affordances Lend Insight into the Big Picture of Nature

Looking at the big pictures of both product design and reverse engineering highlights the importance of relationships, even within the highly technical environments associated with these areas. It also brings into focus the tremendous influence engineers possess, perhaps largely unknowingly, within society. According to "systems thinking," engineers determine the structure of the products they create, and the structure of those products significantly influences the behavior of users.[16] This is true because it is the structure of products that determine their affordances, and the affordances describe what behaviors are possible. In short, structure determines affordances, and affordances describe potential behavior.[17] Thus, the engineer influences the behavior of society by the kinds of products that are designed and the affordances that are engineered into those products.

As a consequence, Maier and Fadel have proposed an affordance-based definition of engineering design. They claim that "design is the specification of a system structure that does possess certain desired affordances in order to support certain desired behaviors, but does not possess certain undesired affordances in order to avoid certain undesired behaviors." As an example, consider the design of an amusement park. Such places are structured to provide affordances such as easy access to attractions; comfort to visitors; convenient access to good food, drink, and necessary facilities; and a minimum amount of walking, all at an affordable price. If a significant amount of walking is required, then beautiful scenery or interesting venues are provided to afford distraction from the burdensome task of legged locomotion. If the distance to be covered is too large, a tram or shuttle is provided to afford comfort and energy savings to the visitors.

These particular affordances are engineered into the park structure in order to elicit certain behavior by visitors. Above all, the park is engineered to ensure that visitors have such an enjoyable time that they will want to return to the park often. Hence, affordances that maximize enjoyment are designed into the park, and affordances that inhibit such enjoyment are minimized. If successfully designed, park visitors will enjoy a variety of attractions in a safe and comfortable setting without spending too much money. In this case, the park owners and engineers have accomplished their purposes by establishing a profitable business that also provides entertainment and recreation to the community.

Perhaps it is helpful to consider the creation of the universe in a similar light, remembering that structure determines affordances, and affordances describe potential behavior. The structure of the universe appears to be engineered to afford life, at least on planet Earth, and perhaps elsewhere. But that is not the only affordance presented by the structure of the universe. Human beings are a very curious lot. We want to know how things work, where we come from, and how this universe got started. In short, the universe also affords wonder and curiosity within humans. At the same time, the universe also seems to afford discovery to human beings. Science has made substantial progress through the ages because humans have acted on these affordances of wonder, curiosity, and discoverability.

Of course, we have a choice in this matter. Just because we perceive an affordance, doesn't mean we will necessarily act on it. This is what determines the difference between user and investigator in the big picture of reverse engineering the universe, or hacking the cosmos. The investigator takes the time and energy to objectively explore the big questions concerning the nature of the universe. The human species is curious about more than just the nuts and bolts of how the universe works. We also wonder what it all means. Are there indications of purpose for the human race? Is there something beyond the material realm? These questions, along with some detailed examples further illustrating the big picture of reverse engineering, will be explored in the remaining chapters.

CHARACTER ENGINEERING CONCLUSIONS

In many ways, the teachers and coaches of my childhood were the engineers of my character during those formative years of my life. They taught me the value of hard work and discipline. They taught me how to set realistic goals, work toward them, and ultimately accomplish them. They also taught me how to handle failure and defeat by recognizing that valuable lessons can be learned from all our experiences.

I have very few memories of the early basketball games in which I played. I must have blotted them out of my memory. Games were enormously stressful, probably because of the inordinate pressure our coaches put on us to win. I have since learned that character formation is to be prized more highly than defeating the opponent. But in those days we were taught that winning was everything. Home games were stressful enough, but away games brought the added anxiety of an unfamiliar court with many more unfamiliar fans.

Before each game, the coach would tell each of us who we would be guarding on defense. He would often remind us that if we would each hold our man to fewer points than we individually scored, we would win the game. We were playing at Chalmers (a small town about thirty minutes north of Lafayette, Indiana) one year and coach assigned me to guard their "big man." He was easy to spot because he was the big guy wearing the large, heavy, metal knee brace. I quickly learned that his favorite move was to receive the ball at the top of the key, and then drive toward the basket with a right-hand dribble for a closer shot. He was obviously Chalmers' favorite son because the home crowd went wild whenever he attempted this move.

Now coach had taught us well how to defend against such a move. So every time he tried it, I quickly moved laterally to my left to cut off his advance. Sometimes I got there first, and sometimes I was a little late to the party. But inevitably, it seemed that he always banged his gimpy knee as a result of our repeated collisions. Often he would drop to the floor and grab his knee, howling in pain. As the game wore on and his limp became more pronounced, I vividly remember the hostile crowd cheering louder and louder for my ejection, and subsequent lynching. Or so it seemed at the time. "What kind of Catholic school is this . . . that teaches their players to aggravate an opponent's injury?" I heard them shouting. Now, I had no ill-will toward this kid. I was just trying to play good defense. I don't even remember how the game turned out. But to have a whole crowd of people crying out for my demise was a rather unsettling experience for a ten-year-old kid. I'm thankful to our coach for reminding me that I wasn't doing anything wrong by playing tenacious defense.

At another away game against the St. Mary's Yellow Jackets, I became so disoriented in the strange gymnasium that I ended up shooting at the wrong basket! I quickly recognized the error of my ways, but it was too late. The damage had been done. To an aspiring basketball star, this was a huge embarrassment, and the epitome of stupidity. Again, I don't remember who won the game, but I do remember after the game; sitting in the locker room after I showered and dressed; I was too embarrassed to come out and face everyone after such an enormous blunder. Eventually my coach asked me why I hadn't left yet, and when I told him, he said, "Forget it; no one will even remember that you shot at the wrong basket." This helped me realize that I was suffering from an unhealthy self-centered state of consciousness. Sure enough, when I summoned the courage to show my face outside the locker room, no one said anything about my great mistake. And it didn't make it into the morning newspaper either.

These incidents, along with many others like them, helped me to avoid arrogance and learn humility as a young person, although I needed to keep learning this lesson over and over again. Fortunately, I had a caring group of coaches, teachers, and advisors who played a big role in the engineering of my character. They structured my activities and environment to afford discipline that ultimately helped me gain wisdom for how to live.

It appears that our natural world is similarly structured. The universe seems engineered to teach us the honest truth about our frailties, and keep us humble. In general, virtuous behavior is rewarded, and vices are not rewarded. We gain a profound sense of satisfaction when we help others, but we experience unrelenting guilt when we behave in ways that we know are wrong. The cosmos is structured to afford knowledge of right and wrong, and knowledge of God. These affordances encourage us to choose what is good, true, and beautiful, but our human nature so often heads in the opposite direction. These deep mysteries will be explored further in the remaining chapters.

STUDY QUESTIONS

1. Describe an embarrassing moment from your childhood. Did anything good come out of it?
2. Briefly analyze the relationships between the three key entities in the big picture of designing an automobile.
3. How is the big picture of engineering design expanded to achieve the big picture of reverse engineering?
4. What lessons were learned in the reverse engineering of the Antikythera Mechanism?
5. How do the relationships between the reverse engineer and the other three entities in the big picture of reverse engineering affect the quality of a reverse engineering project?
6. How do engineers significantly influence the behavior of society?
7. Discuss how positive affordances are maximized and negative affordances are minimized in the design of a major airport terminal building. Describe how typical current terminal designs could be improved in terms of positive and negative affordances.
8. What are key factors that determine the difference between user and investigator in the big picture of reverse-engineering the universe?
9. Describe a time when you experienced adversity. What important lessons did you learn?

ENDNOTES

1. Hebrews 12:11 says, "No discipline seems pleasant at the time, but painful. Later on, however, it produces a harvest of righteousness and peace for those who have been trained by it."

2. Adapted from Jonathan Maier, *Affordance Based Design: Theoretical Foundations and Practical Applications* (Saarbrucken, Germany: VDM Verlag, 2011), 52.

3. Jonathan R. A. Maier and Georges M. Fadel, "Affordance Based Design: A Relational Theory for Design," *Research in Engineering Design* 20 (March 2009): 13.

4. Maier and Fadel, "Affordance Based Design," 19.

5. Maier and Fadel, "Affordance Based Design," 19.

6. Maier and Fadel, "Affordance Based Design," 19–20.

7. Dominic Halsmer, Tyler Todd, and Nate Roman, "Integrating the Concept of Affordance into Function-based Reverse-engineering with Application to Complex Natural Systems," Proceedings of the ASEE Annual Conference, Austin, TX, June 14–17, 2009.

8. http://www.atlasobscura.com/places/antikythera-mechanism.

9. Jo Marchant, *Decoding the Heavens: A 2,000-year-old Computer—and the Century-long Search to Discover its Secrets* (Cambridge, MA: Da Capo Press, 2009). For a comprehensive technical update, see Constantin Stikas, *Antikythera Mechanism—The Book—Unwinding the History of Science and TecÚology* (Athens: Constantin Stikas, 2014).

10. Marchant, *Decoding the Heavens*, 61.

11. Jonathan R. A. Maier and Georges M. Fadel, "Affordance-based Design Methods for Innovative Design, Redesign and Reverse Engineering" *Research in Engineering Design* 20 (March 2009): 225.

12. Maier and Fadel, "Affordance-based Design Methods," 234.

13. Maier and Fadel, "Affordance-based Design Methods," 234–35.

14. Maier and Fadel, "Affordance-based Design Methods," 235.

15. Maier and Fadel, "Affordance-based Design Methods," 231.

16. Jay W. Forrester, *Principles of Systems* (Waltham, MA, Pegasus Communications, 1968).

17. Maier and Fadel, "Affordance Based Design," 23.

CHAPTER NINE

Examples of Affordance-Based Reverse Engineering

FROM MODELS TO UGLIES

From as early as I can remember, my family took annual summertime camping trips to Oshkosh, Wisconsin, to attend the EAA (Experimental Aircraft Association) Fly-in and Air Show. As a kid, this was the event to which I most looked forward, besides Christmas of course. Since a few of my ten older siblings already had their pilot's licenses, some of them might fly private aircraft from our airport to this huge gathering of aviation enthusiasts. But the rest of us rode out the long five-hour drive in the large camping bus our Dad had acquired for just this occasion.[1] We usually got there a few days early to stake out a close camping spot in front of the "warbirds." I considered these historic military aircraft to be one of the highlights of the whole show, along with the exciting aerobatic performances every evening.

A large number of vendors took advantage of the big crowd of airplane-crazy spectators, and to my surprise and delight, some of these vendors sold plastic model airplane kits. This is where I first experienced the joy of building a model airplane, and it became a cherished tradition. Every year, I would scour the exhibits to find the most worthy airplane model to build. Then I would lay down my hard-earned grass-cutting money for the kit and the necessary paints and tools.

A card table and folding lawn chair under the tarp stretched out from the side of our bus served as an adequate workspace. This early model-building experience was particularly pleasing if the model represented a military aircraft that was actually at the air show. I found it sublimely satisfying to construct an accurate model of such an exciting and complex piece of machinery. This satisfaction was enhanced considerably if the model had authentically moving parts, such as spinning propellers, folding wings, rotating gun turrets, or retractable landing gears.

Perhaps I have just never really grown up, but I still consider plastic model kits to be extremely cool. Once the thin plastic shrink-wrapping material is removed, the top of the box is lifted off and the extent of the required assembly is immediately revealed. The more pieces there are, the more assembly is required, and the longer it will take to complete. One of the most complex kits is Revell's scale replica of the famous War of 1812-era frigate *USS Constitution* containing 1,223 parts.[2] These parts are not just thrown into the box like so many pieces of a jigsaw puzzle, but instead are typically numbered and (usually) remain lightly attached to the plastic frame, or "tree," with which they were molded. Multiple trees of parts may be found in a single kit, along with finishing decals and assembly instructions.

One of the reasons these kits afford such satisfaction is the precision with which they are engineered and manufactured. Revell boasts that its computer-generated part specifications are reproduced in plastic to an accuracy of three-thousandths of an inch (.003 inches)![3] This requirement ensures a virtually perfect fit between parts, such that all these part-to-part affordances result in a completed whole model that possesses no cracks, offsets, or other clues of being assembled from many parts. Thus, with careful assembly and attention to detail, the end-user is afforded a very realistic, though much smaller, replica of the actual vehicle.

What makes model-building so rewarding? Recent scientific studies have identified an area of the human brain called the "effort-driven rewards circuit"[4] that, when activated, may help in avoiding depression. An article in *Psychology Today* notes that this circuit is driven by "physical activities that involve our hands, particularly activities that produce tangible products that we can see, touch, and enjoy."[5] Furthermore, "'making things' such as a drawing, painting, collage, weaving, or sculpture involve hands-on investment in an object with tangible results that give pleasure to or have meaning for their creators."[6] Thus, building with our hands affords pleasure and satisfaction while also discouraging depression and despair. As an engineer, I have experienced this effect firsthand. As an engineering professor, I assign projects that allow our students to experience these positive sensations. It seems that the capacity and drive to be creators is engineered into our DNA, reinforced by our neuronal circuitry, and activated by working with our hands. Perhaps this is part of what it means for humans to be made in the image of God.

Several of my siblings also enjoyed model-building, and we continued this pursuit after we got home from the air show. The corner of our basement was turned into an engineering laboratory with an adequate store of tools and equipment. Early on in my model-building career, I noticed one piece of equipment that piqued my curiosity. It was a simple candle. I soon learned from watching my older brothers that a little heat from a candle flame affords targeted softening to plastic parts so that they can be easily bent or reshaped as needed. This is a delicate process since a little more heat affords a rapid phase transformation in which the plastic changes from solid to liquid drops of a sizzling hot lava-like substance. And just the right amount of heat applied to two pieces of plastic affords a rapid and virtually permanent connection when quickly pressed together. Such heat-assisted bonding, though somewhat crude and imprecise, affords rapid assembly as the plastic joint cools quickly and becomes rigid once again. We soon realized that with a little bit of practice, these affordances could lead to a much more creative activity in which original designs could be speedily produced from leftover model trees and unused plastic parts.

Perhaps America's obsession with space aliens in the 1960s and '70s helps to explain why so many alien-like plastic creatures arose out of those flames. Whatever the reason, Mom took one look at an early creation and christened it based on its looks. She called it an "ugly," and the name stuck. It came to represent anything that was engineered out of plastic in our basement laboratory via candle power. I particularly enjoyed the engineering of such strange and wonderful creations, and quickly spread the word that model trees and unused parts were no longer trash to be thrown out after a model was finished. Instead, they were the precious raw materials of some heretofore unforeseen adorable plastic mutant. Before long, there were several "uglies" lining the mantle of our fireplace in the breezeway entrance to our house. At the time, I was quite proud of my laborious contributions to our home décor. Now I wonder what visitors must have thought, and my appreciation for Mom's patience and grace has expanded considerably.

Upon further thought, uglies were simply the next logical step in our creative progress. Assembling a model kit by following the instructions can be very satisfying, but beyond the application of an original paint job, there's not much room for creativity. By contrast, the uglies were completely original; something that no one had ever thought of before, and there were no instructions to follow. The possibilities were limitless. This same contrast is seen in two competing streams of thought when building with Lego bricks. There are Lego kits that come with specific detailed step-by-step instructions, but some builders prefer the pursuit of original creations that only preexist in their imaginations.[7]

In a sense, we had reverse-engineered and reengineered the standard plastic model kit in that old basement laboratory. We explored its full potential and found new ways to improve on its capacity to provide enjoyment while also fostering creativity. Through application of the world's most primitive energy source—fire—to one of the world's most recent materials—plastic—we engineered new parts for brand new objects that had never before been conceived. And we fabricated those objects according to the original patterns in our minds, based on the affordances at hand. Of course, fire has some *negative* affordances as well, and that led to a monumental mishap on one of my early modeling attempts. But before I share that story, let's explore some other examples of affordance-based reverse engineering.

Queen of the Tamagotchis

This chapter describes several examples of affordance-based reverse engineering. Both artificial and natural systems are considered. Ultimately, this book attempts to apply this approach to better understand the implications of our resource-rich universe, which appears to find the emergence and sustenance of complex life quite "affordable," at least on planet Earth, and perhaps elsewhere. In this sense, the universe is a "big spender!" The point of anthropomorphizing the cosmos like this is not to suggest that it has any innate creative powers of its own, but to once again emphasize the curiously complex nested affordance structures that exist at all observable levels. We will start by looking at examples involving human-engineered systems, and then consider the more intriguing case of natural systems.

The simple example from the previous section presented the plastic model kit as the product that was, in the described sense, reverse-engineered and reengineered, resulting in a new "product" called "uglies." Recalling the big picture of reverse engineering laid out in the previous chapter, the original engineer is a plastic model kit-producing company, such as Revell. The end-user is the model-building community. And the investigators, or reverse-engineers, are my siblings and I.

Of course, we weren't thinking in terms of affordance-based reverse engineering at the time, but we recognized those key relationships (i.e., fire to plastic) that resulted in the desired capabilities (i.e., melting and bonding), which is the definition of affordances. And we used those relationships to better understand how the kit could be used to create original designs, which is a form of affordance-based reverse engineering and reengineering. Recall also that a thorough investigation into all the relationships between product, original engineer, end user, and investigator would lend further insight into this reverse engineering effort.[8] But now it's time to move on to some more complex and interesting examples.

I was recently scanning the internet for examples of reverse engineering when I discovered the extraordinary work of Natalie Silvanovich, who has become known as the "Queen of the Tamagotchis." In case you missed out on this worldwide techno-toy fad that started in the 1990s, a Tamagotchi is a handheld digital "pet" invented in Japan and produced by Bandai, a large Japanese toy company. Users play this virtual pet simulation game by interacting with an image of the creature on a small screen via multiple buttons. The creature goes through several stages of growth, and will develop differently depending on the type of care provided by the player, with better care resulting in a smarter, happier, and healthier adult creature.[9] Apparently, Tamagotchis were originally designed for teenage girls, to give them an idea of what it might be like to take care of children.[10]

Natalie Silvanovich is a nerdy, but strangely charming, information security engineer at Google who uses her electrical and computer engineering background to hack Tamagotchis in her spare time. At this point, let me just take a moment to warn all Tamagotchis everywhere that a more appropriate title for Ms. Silvanovich would be the "White Witch[11] of the Tamagotchis," having seen what she does to these poor creatures once she lures them into her secret kitchen laboratory. Seriously, to be fair, she readily admits as much in the title of her presentation at REcon 2013,[13] "Many Tamagotchis Were Harmed in the Making of this Presentation."[12] One of the reasons I love this example is because of her obvious passion for uncovering hidden knowledge via reverse engineering, a skill that requires much dedication and perseverance. Again, this is clear from her talk, her nerdy voice squeaking through, loud and proud, as she explains one of the main reasons for her eccentric hobby. "And finally, I just wanted to have fun, because you know all those cool kids, going out, going to clubs . . . they just haven't discovered reverse engineering yet."[14] And all the nerds in the audience clapped and cheered as wildly as their technologically oriented psyches would allow.

Other reasons she gives for the unusual amount of time and energy she devotes to hacking Tamagotchis are, "I wanted to answer the 'deeper questions' of Tamagotchi life" and "I wanted to make my Tamagotchis the richest and happiest Tamagotchis ever!"[15] As I watched her presentation on the internet, I began to appreciate and relate to her work, because of my own interest in applying reverse engineering to answer the deeper questions of biological life, and the cosmos that supports this life. Notice the direct parallel between her work and the aims of this book. Notice also her desire to reengineer her Tamagotchis, implementing improvements, based on the knowledge she gained, to make them richer and happier. Likewise, the goal of this book is to equip the reader with knowledge and insight that will lead to a richer, happier existence. If reverse engineering can be applied to help answer the deeper questions of Tamagotchi life, then perhaps it can also be applied to help answer the deeper questions of biological, and even human, life.

Now, the intricate details of her reverse engineering exploits are well beyond the scope of this book. But suffice it to say that she has been very successful thus far, in dissecting several Tamagotchis, and skillfully teasing apart the hardware and software elements to uncover the hierarchy of nested affordances that flow from the elemental relationships. Consider again the big picture of reverse engineering, and apply it to this example. The product is the Tamagotchi. The original engineer is Bandai, and other companies that engineered the embedded computer chips. The end user is the group of customers (mostly young girls) who purchased and played with the Tamagotchi. And the investigator in this case is Natalie Silvanovich, whose training in engineering gave her the confidence to start such a monumental task, and whose determination carried her through to a satisfying completion. By the time she was finished, she even had her Tamagotchis doing the *Harlem Shake*. They must have been very happy Tamagotchis indeed.

The big picture of reverse engineering for this example is shown below in Figure 9–1.

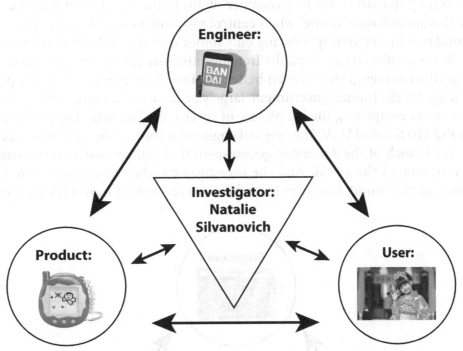

Figure 9–1   The Big Picture of Reverse-Engineering Tamagotchis
Source: ©Shutterstock.com

A brief look at the relationships between these four entities helps to illustrate and illuminate the reality of the situation. Obviously, Bandai has intimate knowledge of the Tamagotchis they created. And they use their knowledge of customer buying patterns and desires (often obtained through surveys and focus groups) to make their Tamagotchis as attractive as possible to the end users. It is easy to see how the three outer relationships in the diagram are critically important for successful engineering product design. This represents the big picture of engineering design.

But what about the three inner relationships between the investigator and the other three entities? It is these relationships that shed further light on the product, how it works, and why it was created. In this case, the investigator, Natalie Silvanovich, probably played with Tamagotchis, along with her friends when she was younger, which gives her firsthand knowledge of the typical end user.

But it was her relationship with the actual Tamagotchi that afforded wonder and curiosity about how it works. And her knowledge of the toy increased exponentially as she dissected many of them, and probed their inner workings. Her attempts to form relationships with Bandai and the computer chip manufacturers, in order to gather helpful information, were generally rejected due to company private policies. Thus, she was not able to acquire much useful data from the original engineers. Even so, her expertise and determination brought success in one of the more interesting examples of modern-day reverse engineering and reengineering.

The Case of the Captured Drone

As described in Chapter Seven, military technology provides an arena in which attempts are continually being made to reverse-engineer an adversary's latest weapons systems. As a recent example, consider the capture of the American RQ 170 *Sentinel* unmanned aerial vehicle (UAV—made by Lockheed Martin) by Iranian forces in December of 2011. The Central Intelligence Agency (CIA) was operating this surveillance "drone" when control was somehow lost, and it unexpectedly ended up on the ground in Iran, apparently suffering only minor damage. Delighted to have acquired some of the latest military aviation technology, the Iranians immediately commenced reverse engineering activities, in an effort to reengineer an even better version of their own.[16] This has proved to be an immense challenge for the Iranian government, largely because of the nature of the relationships that connect the elements comprising the big picture of reverse engineering. The product in this case is the American RQ 170 *Sentinel* UAV. The original engineer is the Lockheed Martin Corporation. The user is the CIA, a branch of the American government that gathers and analyzes national security information from around the world. And the investigator is the Iranian government, depicted in Figure 9–2 below as Mahmoud Ahmadinejad, who was president of Iran at the time of the capture.

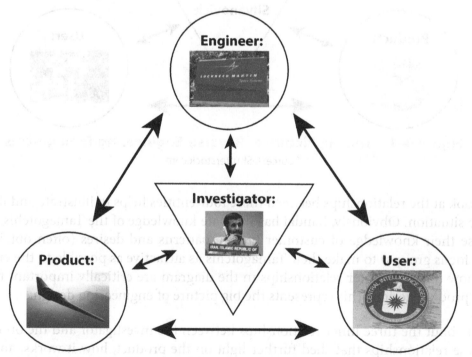

Figure 9–2   The Big Picture of Reverse-Engineering the RQ 170 *Sentinel*
Source: ©Shutterstock.com

As expected, Lockheed Martin has intimate knowledge of the RQ 170 *Sentinel*, since they engineered it from the ground up. And normal customer relations between Lockheed Martin and the CIA entail documentation and training sufficient for CIA staff to have operational knowledge of the *Sentinel*. But Mahmoud Ahmadinejad made it quite clear during his presidency of Iran that he was no friend of America. During this time, the American and Iranian governments were engaged in a very adversarial and antagonistic relationship. Given this climate, the relationship between Iran and Lockheed Martin would be virtually nonexistent, making it difficult, if not impossible, to gain detailed technical data concerning the *Sentinel*.

Modern military aircraft are very complex, and are often computer-controlled, which adds to the difficulty of any reverse engineering effort. In addition, computer software and data stored on the *Sentinel* would typically be encrypted by the software security engineers at Lockheed Martin. This affords another level of difficulty, though it may not be insurmountable, especially if Iran was able to get help from other countries such as Russia and China. Since Iran now has direct access to an only slightly damaged *Sentinel*, they are highly motivated to take advantage of this opportunity, and they have made some progress. Iranian scientists and engineers have continued to explore the relationships within and between *Sentinel* subsystems that afford high performance flight and reconnaissance. In November of 2014, they claimed to have executed a successful test flight of an aircraft based on information gleaned from reverse-engineering the *Sentinel*.[17] Thus, even in an adversarial environment with only a single damaged specimen, reverse engineering efforts can still pay off to some degree.

Reverse-Engineering the Worm

The previous examples dealt with products (model kits, Tamagotchis, and a *Sentinel* drone) of human creativity and ingenuity. Perhaps these human-made products are readily reverse-engineered by humans because they were also engineered by humans. This would help to explain the match between product complexity and the ability of the investigator to unravel and understand that complexity. Such a match is a necessary prerequisite for the success of any reverse engineering project. But what about products that humans discover in the natural realm? Great progress has also been made in reverse-engineering these systems. Biological systems, in particular, have yielded many secrets as biologists and engineers have worked together to uncover the complex relationships that allow us to enjoy all the affordances of life.

In studying the mysteries of life, researchers dissect specimens that are simple enough to facilitate insight, and yet complicated enough to provide helpful information about even more complex organisms such as human beings. The planarian (flatworm) is a good example of just such a specimen that has been studied extensively for more than a century. Flatworms are relatively simple organisms, but with an intricate body-plan and nervous system that allows them to do amazing things; such as perfectly regenerate limbs, brains, and other complex body parts after traumatic injury.[18] Motivation for studying the flatworm is provided in a recent review article. "Individual planarians are practically immortal—able to regenerate aging, as well as severely damaged or lost, tissues. A trunk fragment cut from the middle of an adult planarian will regenerate into a whole worm, always growing a new head and new tail in the same orientation as the original worm. As little as 1/279th of a planarian, or a fragment with as few as 10,000 cells, can regenerate into a new worm within one to two weeks. Thus, reverse-engineering the remarkable system that is planarian regeneration would have profound impacts on regenerative medicine, bioengineering, synthetic biology, and robotics."[19]

The authors of this review article on planarian regeneration also recognized the need to encourage engineers and other technologists to enter this specialized field of biology. They write, "To facilitate modeling efforts by computer scientists, physicists, engineers and mathematicians, we present a different kind of review of planarian regeneration. Focusing on the main patterning properties of this system, we review what is known about the signal exchanges that occur during regenerative repair in planaria and the cellular mechanisms that are thought to underlie them. By establishing an engineering-like style for reviews of the molecular developmental biology of biomedically important model systems, significant fresh insights and quantitative computational models will be developed by new collaborations between biology and the information sciences."[20]

The "signal exchanges" and their underlying "cellular mechanisms" mentioned by the authors indicate their desire to understand the relationships between the elements of the system that afford such amazing regenerative capabilities. Applying affordance-based reverse engineering techniques in an intentional manner should assist in such efforts. Indeed, it represents a direct response to their explicit appeal for new methods. "A fresh set of ideas may be helpful, from areas of science that have developed techniques for reverse-engineering complex systems, utilizing analytical methods and types of models that are distinct from those familiar to most cell biologists today."[21] Determining the relationships that produce the signaling and other mechanisms that establish the nested affordance hierarchy within the flatworm is the core activity of this project.

In an effort to further identify these relationships, two of the authors (from Tufts University) developed a computer simulation of the flatworm, incorporating what is already known of its regenerative systems into the model.[22] This computer model was also able to change in many different ways as they attempted to reproduce the known experimental results. The process is described in a *Wired* article. "It simulated the network formed by the worm's genes many times over until its results matched those from real-life experiments. Every time it managed to match [some] results, the computer modified the random genetic network it had created in line with the results and kept honing it until it created a core genetic network that matched the results of all the studies. This took three days of trial and error guessing and tweaking—an approach that would be unfathomably inefficient if it were implemented by humans."[23]

The unique aspect of this project is how the computer greatly assisted in the reverse engineering, as described in another article. "The discovery by Tufts University biologists presents the first model of regeneration discovered by a non-human intelligence and the first comprehensive model of planarian regeneration, which has eluded human scientists for over 100 years. The work . . . demonstrates how 'robot science' can help human scientists in the future."[24] But the computer wasn't just used for crunching numbers. It was actually instrumental in identifying the part-to-part affordances that endow the flatworm with such fantastic regenerative capabilities. According to co-author Michael Levin, "All this suggests to me that artificial intelligence can help with every aspect of science, not only data mining but also inference of meaning of the data."[25] Perhaps computers may be able to assist humans in answering some of the "big questions" that arise from scientific research.

One of those big questions has to do with origins. From where do these amazing natural systems ultimately come? They exhibit incredible efficiency and ingenuity. They possess hierarchical nested affordance structures that result in tremendous value. They readily lend themselves to human attempts at reverse engineering, which generally prove very profitable. All this points to the existence and influence of a cosmic engineer with expertise and capabilities that far exceed those of human engineers. In terms of affordances, humanity's relationship with nature affords knowledge of an engineering mastermind behind the cosmos. Thus, with reference to the big picture of reverse engineering where the product is a flatworm, the original engineer is hypothesized to be a Maker with sufficient engineering expertise to produce such systems.[26] Given that flatworms play an important role in watercourse ecosystems and are often very important as bio-indicators,[27] the end user could be taken as all of life, in general, and human life, in particular. And the investigator is represented by all those who have studied the flatworm over the years, but especially the two Tufts researchers, Daniel Lobo and Michael Levin, who engineered this most recent exemplary breakthrough. Figure 9–3 below illustrates this big picture.

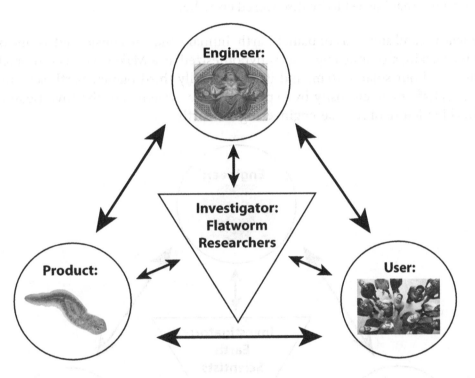

Figure 9–3   The Big Picture of Reverse-Engineering the Flatworm Regenerative System
Source: ©Shutterstock.com

Consider the interesting relationships between the investigator and the other entities that make up the big picture of reverse engineering the flatworm. As a member of the human race, the investigator also enjoys and appreciates the role of end user, recognizing that the flatworm is an important part of the global ecosystem that supports all life on this planet. But the investigator goes further by asking deeper questions about natural systems, and investing the time and effort it takes to answer those questions. Investigators are driven by the wonder and curiosity that these natural systems evoke. Flatworm investigators are also interested in reengineering since they hope to discover regenerative mechanisms that can be implemented in humans to improve our capacity to respond to injuries.

But investigators wonder about more than just how natural systems work. The ingenious mechanisms for regeneration in the flatworm are just one example of the marvelous ingenuity extending throughout the entire realm of nature. This leads investigators, as well as inquisitive end users, to wonder about the origin of these systems. Unfortunately, the original (cosmic) Engineer is not physically available for an interview regarding the creation of natural systems. But that has not stopped many people from pursuing a vital spiritual relationship with their Maker. And the investigation of natural systems appears to play an important role in facilitating this relationship.

Planet Fitness

Another natural system that causes us to wonder about origins is the planet we call home. As our observation and understanding of outer space has developed, humans have come to appreciate planet Earth as a lush vibrant oasis in an otherwise barren and life-threatening environment. Earth scientists study the various parts of the earth (including the atmosphere and moon), how it all fits together, and how it came to be here. Perhaps there are aliens in other parts of the universe, but the relationships between Earth's subsystems and other parts of our solar system afford a persistent kind of carbon-based life that has yet to be discovered elsewhere.

As beneficiaries and stewards of planet Earth, humans may be considered as one of the primary end users. Once again, a cosmic engineer is hypothesized as a Maker who is ultimately responsible for the existence of our solar system, and its life-friendly third planet. Earth scientists and others who regularly satisfy their curiosity by exploring these systems are the investigators. Figure 9–4 illustrates this big picture of reverse-engineering the earth.

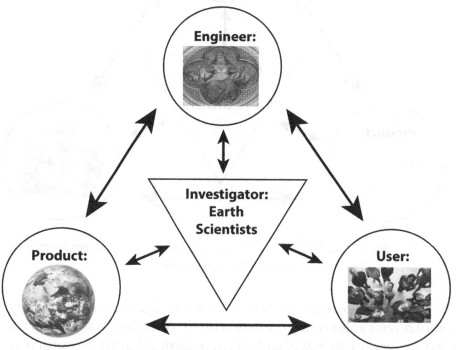

Figure 9–4   The Big Picture of Reverse-Engineering the Earth
Source: ©Shutterstock.com

As described in Chapter Five, the Earth-Moon system forms a beneficial relationship that results in many affordances that help to support life on Earth. The relationship between the atmosphere and the planet affords a stable water cycle that affords irrigation and agriculture, which affords food production, which affords life. The relationship between plants and animals affords the simultaneous production of oxygen and carbon dioxide, which affords respiration, which affords life. The relationship between the oceans and the continental land masses affords moderate temperatures across the globe, which also affords life. These are just a few of the nested affordances associated with planet Earth that result in a fitness for life. As end users, humans should seek to ensure that these life-sustaining affordances are maintained, and refrain from activities that would tend to damage or eliminate their beneficial effects.

Life, the Universe and Everything

Up to this point we have considered both human-made products and natural products, but what if we consider the entire universe as the product? Multiple religious perspectives agree that a Maker (or Cosmic Engineer) is responsible for bringing all things into existence "in the beginning."[28] And since the universe appears to be engineered to support the emergence of complex life, it is tempting to suggest that human beings are the end users. Indeed, from an anthropocentric point of view, we are. But consider another common religious view, that the Creator has made all things *for himself.*[29] In this perhaps more fundamental sense, the original (cosmic) Engineer is also the ultimate end user. This is not an unusual situation to imagine. Human engineers often make things for themselves, and this familiar arrangement may help us as we continue in our attempt at hacking the cosmos.

So who is the investigator in this case? It can only be the human race. We are the ones with the capacity to decipher many of the mysteries of the universe, and contemplate the big questions relating to origins. Recall that Albert Einstein noted this curious state-of-affairs when he famously quipped, "The most incomprehensible thing about the world is that it is comprehensible." To one degree or another, everyone investigates the world around them in order to function in everyday life. Those who continue their education, whether in the sciences, the humanities, or some other field, inevitably uncover additional secrets about some aspect of the universe. According to Christianity, this is exactly what the cosmic engineer intended. The Creator has made his existence, and something of his attributes, plain to everyone, as we steadily apprehend and comprehend the world. But we all tend to suppress this truth; another unfortunate aspect of our human condition.[30] This big picture of hacking the cosmos is illustrated in Figure 9–5 below.

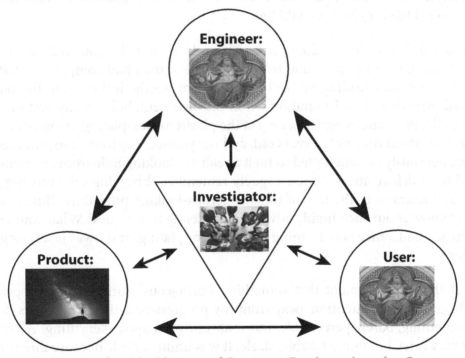

Figure 9–5   The Big Picture of Reverse-Engineering the Cosmos
Source: ©Shutterstock.com

Let's take a step back and consider the implications of this big picture. A cosmic engineer has enabled our existence by creating the universe for us, but also for himself. If this is the case, then any legitimate purposes that human beings, or the universe as a whole, might have should emanate from the original engineer. If we are being engineered by someone who is making us for himself, then basically we are his, and his purposes stand, regardless of our own ideas of purpose. But, like the investigators of the Antikythera Mechanism who had no handbook or user's manual to provide additional information, we don't get much information about purpose from the universe. We do perceive our powerful and unique ability to love as an important clue to our ultimate purpose. But this is only a clue. If a Cosmic Engineer has set this whole thing up, it seems reasonable that more specific information about our purpose would be communicated. This is why many people think it is reasonable to expect such details in the form of a divinely inspired text that has been compiled and passed down through history. This model of reality, along with its associated challenges, will be explored further in the remaining chapters.

PUSHING THE MODELING ENVELOPE

Models of reality can be very helpful in answering life's big questions, but every model has its limitations. And when pushed beyond their limits, they tend to break down in ways that can be very unhelpful. It turns out that the same is true for plastic models. Ninety percent of the models I built while growing up were airplanes, but once in a while I would try my hand at a ship or a tank. One of my very best replicas was a 1/48th scale World War II German Panzer IV tank, exquisitely molded in fine detail by Tamiya Plastic Model Company. I spent countless hours carefully assembling and painting this most treasured creation, with numerous finishing touches to make it the very best it could be.

Even as a kid, I was already doing research on how to make your military models even more realistic by simulating "wear and tear" and battle scars. I had completed my Panzer tank months earlier, but after reading up on this topic, I presently decided that the tank was not quite finished. And that's how I found myself in the basement, holding my best model directly above the candle, the flame hungrily licking at the plastic armor-plating on one side of the tank. I must have been about nine or ten years old, and my younger (by four years) brother, Tim, was watching me nervously as I attempted to melt a realistic-looking hole from an enemy shell that had pierced the thick armor plating. I vaguely remember shrugging off Tim's urgent appeals for caution and restraint in the face of this dangerous-looking procedure. But what could my little brother know about such highly advanced modeling techniques? What could possibly go wrong? I already had a nice hole forming in the armor plating, and I was just trying to make it a little bigger.

It was at that very moment that something outrageously unexpected happened, which immediately grabbed my attention away from my progressive artistic endeavors. It was just a tiny little something, barely perceptible, but it abruptly changed everything. All of a sudden, there was a very brief, but unmistakable, sizzle. It was unmistakable because three of my senses conspired together to confirm its existence. My senses were already heightened, and focused in on the action of the flame tip on the model, but that focus, along with the thin line of rising black smoke and the pungent smell of burning plastic were immediately overwhelmed by three things: firstly, my eyes caught sight of a tiny intermittent flash of light, deep within the body of the tank, secondly, my ears picked up on a sizzling sound that could only be produced by a couple of things, and this certainly wasn't bacon, and thirdly, my nose detected the faint fragrance of burning sulfur, charcoal, and potassium nitrate (a mixture better known as gun powder). This was a very curious development, indeed.

Actually, it only took a fraction of a second for all this curious data to become reconciled in my mind, and for me to realize the extreme gravity and intense irony of the situation in which I suddenly found myself. Now, I'm not trying to offer any excuses, but let me at least try to explain how this absurd event could have possibly occurred. Our family really excelled at celebrating holidays. Lots of presents at Christmas, egg hunts on Easter, and family fireworks on the Fourth of July. Independence Day was one of my favorite holidays because of the fireworks and associated activities. One ill-conceived but long-standing tradition was to light a sparkler and take off running with it around the perimeter of our large front yard and see if we could get all the way back to the start before it burned out. Let's see, running at breakneck speed, in the dark on uneven ground, while holding a burning metal wire. Not sure who's idea that was, but I enjoyed it tremendously.

During that era, anything more serious than a sparkler was illegal in the state of Indiana, but that didn't stop my older brothers from celebrating in grand fashion. Throughout the year, any occasion to travel out of state was a cherished opportunity to stock up on firecrackers, cherry bombs, and other high-powered pyrotechnics. If they got the chance, they would buy large packs of firecrackers and light them off all-at-once for an extended explosive barrage. On such occasions, I noticed that not all the firecrackers exploded, a few having their lit fuses partially blown off during the initial blast. I had found a couple of these "duds" on the ground the day after our celebration. But knowing full well that I was too young, and therefore not allowed to have firecrackers, I had to find a top secret hiding place in which to store my treasure. As you have probably already guessed by now, the removable rotating turret of my prized Panzer IV model tank provided the perfect little treasure chest for this clandestine maneuver.

I'm not sure what I had in mind for those leftover firecrackers since they only had little nubs of fuse left. So I simply dropped them into the compartment typically reserved for a squad of little tank operators, put the turret back on, and forgot about them until that sizzle. That sizzle was the sound of the nub of a firecracker fuse being lit. Then my previous decisions all flooded back over me like a tsunami on a sand castle. Upon realizing that my sins had found me out, while still holding the tank above the flame, I immediately looked over and made eye contact with little Tim. I didn't know if he had perceived the sizzle or not, but my eyes must have communicated our imminent demise, because he also became wide-eyed with fear. I knew what was about to happen, and I knew it was going to happen very quickly, since those fuses were so dangerously short.

The smartest thing to do would have been to immediately "chuck" that model tank, recently turned armed bomb, across the basement. But that is exactly what you would never do with a carefully crafted model to which you had devoted many hours. This instinct to hold on to the model was too strong to overcome. As I squeezed my eyes closed, turned my head to the side, and locked my elbows to hold the tank out at arm's length, a small, but very realistic, vestige of war resurfaced momentarily within the (normally friendly) confines our basement. The tank exploded with a loud boom that sent a hundred small pieces of plastic shrapnel shooting in every direction. I felt several pieces sting my face and arms, and Tim got hit by a few pieces too. But fortunately, we suffered no permanent physical injuries from this incident, although psychologically, who knows?

I opened my eyes to see my hands at the end of my outstretched arms, appearing to hold some invisible object. But there was just empty space where the tank used to be. I looked over at Tim again and he started to cry. I wanted to cry, but instead rushed over to console Tim and see if he was all right. After a few seconds, our mom's voice was heard urgently inquiring down the basement stairwell. "WHAT WAS THAT NOISE!?" I didn't know how to respond, the truth not seeming to be appropriate at the time, so I thought up a lie and I thought it up quick.[31] I shouted back in the direction of the stairwell, "I just dropped something. Everything's okay." I doubt that my fib really fooled the (old) girl,[32] but she must have been too busy to come down the stairs, and she pressed the issue no further.

Whenever things like this happen in my life, I try to ask myself, "What have I learned from this experience?" Evidently, I *was* too young to manage fireworks safely. My parents had good reasons for this rule, and I should have minded them. And it was a somewhat dangerous technique I was using to put just one more finishing touch on my model. I should have removed that armor plate before attempting to modify it. Or I should have just been satisfied with the model as it was, instead of pushing it past the breaking point. Models of reality have their breaking points as well.

Gary Larson produced a well-known comic (found by going to https://twitter.com/TheTweet OfGod/status/278544128898367489 and scrolling down) that reminds me both of this crazy childhood incident and of limitations of our models of a Maker. It depicts a stunned child with blackened face before a smoking pile of ash and a broken chemistry set. White poultry feathers are silently floating down all around him. Larson, who's witty captions are every bit as good as his outstanding illustrations, writes, "God as a kid tries to make a chicken in his room." Coincidently, the Twitter page cited above is actually purported to be that of God himself! And his most recent tweet recounts his dream of last night, when he had a test on how to create the universe and he forgot to study. Several irreverent, but insightful, replies to this tweet illuminate the diversity of thinking regarding the level of God's engineering skills.

We've been exploring a model of reality in which some kind of engineering mastermind has created this complex cosmos. But all our experience with complicated engineering projects relates to those that are conducted by human engineers. So it's easy to make the mistake of attributing human traits and frailties to this cosmic engineer, who is obviously not human. As mentioned earlier, such technical expertise and wisdom appears to far exceed that of humans. This should give us confidence that this Maker knows what he's doing. He can make a chicken without blowing it up, and he won't forget where he stored his explosives.

STUDY QUESTIONS

1. Describe something you learned to do as a child that activated your effort-driven rewards circuit. Do you still enjoy doing this?

2. How does Silvanovich's reverse engineering work on Tamagotchis parallel the objectives of this book?

3. Discuss the conditions that made Iranian attempts to reverse engineer the RQ-170 drone extremely challenging.

4. Describe how researchers were able to identify the part-to-part affordances that result in the flatworm's amazing regenerative capabilities.

5. What drives investigators to reverse engineer natural systems such as the regenerative capabilities of the flatworm?

6. Describe some of the nested affordances that contribute to the end-user affordance of "livability" on planet Earth.

7. In the big picture of reverse engineering the universe, who would you say is the user? Who is the investigator? Are some humans more investigative than others?

8. Some philosophers suggest that humans can determine their own purposes for their lives. Do you agree? Why or why not?

9. Why would the existence of a divinely inspired text be a reasonable expectation to draw from hacking the cosmos?

10. Describe a stupid mistake you made as a child. What lessons did you learn?

11. Larson's comic raises a sobering question, especially in light of scriptural passages such as Genesis 6:5–6. Is God a poor engineer? What do you think?

ENDNOTES

1. Over the years, we enjoyed multiple editions of a school bus that had been converted into a primitive kind of recreational vehicle. An early version came complete with triple-decker bunk beds.

2. Jeff Greenwald, "Parts and Recreation," *Craftsmanship* (Spring 2015), craftsmanship.net/parts-recreation.

3. Greenwald, "Parts and Recreation."

4. Kelly Lambert, *Lifting Depression: A Neuroscientist's Hands-on Approach to Activating Your Brain's Healing Power* (New York, Basic Books, 2008), 7.

5. Cathy Malchiodi, "Drawing on the Effort-Driven Rewards Circuit to Chase the Blues Away," *Psychology Today* (August 4, 2008), https://www.psychologytoday.com/blog/arts-and-health/200808/drawing-the-effort-driven-rewards-circuit-chase-the-blues-away.

6. Malchiodi, "Drawing on the Effort-Driven Rewards Circuit."

7. *The Lego Movie* (2014) made much hilarity of this philosophical difference of opinion.

8. In this case, an end user is also the investigator, which often occurs, but need not be the case.

9. https://en.wikipedia.org/wiki/Tamagotchi.

10. "Finding Companionship in a Digital Age," *Next Generation* (October 1997): 56–63.

11. With reference to a notorious villain from *The Chronicles of Narnia,* by C. S. Lewis.

12. REcon is a computer security conference, held annually in Montreal, with a focus on reverse engineering and advanced exploitation techniques, https://recon.cx/.

13. https://www.youtube.com/watch?v=WOJfUcCOhJ0.

14. https://www.youtube.com/watch?v=WOJfUcCOhJ0.

15. https://www.youtube.com/watch?v=WOJfUcCOhJ0.

16. https://en.wikipedia.org/wiki/Iran%E2%80%93U.S._RQ-170_incident.

17. https://en.wikipedia.org/wiki/Iran%E2%80%93U.S._RQ-170_incident.

18. Daniel Lobo, Wendy S. Beane, and Michael Levin, "Modeling Planarian Regeneration: A Primer for Reverse-Engineering the Worm," *PLoS Computational Biology* 8, no. 4 (April 26, 2012), doi:10.1371/journal.pcbi.1002481.

19. Lobo, Beane, and Levin, "Modeling Planarian Regeneration."

20. Lobo, Beane, and Levin, "Modeling Planarian Regeneration."

21. Lobo, Beane, and Levin, "Modeling Planarian Regeneration."

22. Daniel Lobo and Michael Levin, "Inferring Regulatory Networks from Experimental Morphological Phenotypes: A Computational Method Reverse-Engineers Planarian Regeneration," *PLoS Computational Biology* 11, no. 6 (November 24, 2014), doi:10.1371/journal.pcbi. 1004295.

23. Katie Collins, "Computer Independently Solves 120-year-old Biological Mystery," *Wired* (June 5, 2015), http://www.wired.co.uk/article/computer-develops-scientific-theory-independently.

24. Kim Thurler, "Planarian Regeneration Model Discovered by Artificial Intelligence," *TuftsNow* (June 4, 2015), http://now.tufts.edu/news-releases/planarian-regeneration-model-discovered-artificial-intelligence.

25. Thurler, "Planarian Regeneration Model Discovered by Artificial Intelligence."

26. The image used in the figure is a classic piece of artwork from the thirteenth century known as "God as Architect/Builder/Geometer/Craftsman." It was originally created for the frontispiece of the Bible Moralisee.

27. Raoul Manenti, "Effect of Landscape Features and Water Quality on Triclads Inhabiting Head Waters: The Example of *Polycelis Felina,*" *Revue Ecologie Terre et Vie* 65 (2010): 279–285. Bioindicators provide a measure of the health of the ecosystem in which they reside.

28. With reference to the first words of the Bible, Genesis 1:1.

29. See Colossians 1:16, for example.

30. Romans 1:18–20.

31. Dr. Seuss, *How the Grinch Stole Christmas* (New York, Random House, 1957).

32. Seuss, *How the Grinch Stole Christmas.*

PART IV

Philosophical and Theological Implications

CHAPTER TEN

Challenges to the Idea of an Engineered World

DRAFTED INTO THE GRASS CUTTING CORP

One spring day when I was young, my older brother, Robert, began to take an inordinate interest in the level of my fledgling physical strength. "Can you push it?" he barked as he nodded toward the handle of an early-model gas-powered push mower. Seeking to demonstrate the adequacy of my marginal strength, I threw everything I had into that handle, which hit me just below the chin. As I leaned into it, slowly the mower began to roll through the already thick and lengthening grass. "Good, you're ready," he concluded. Then he added, "Be at the dining room table in ten minutes."

Had I realized what I was getting myself into, I might not have attacked that mower handle with such fervor. Later, I would wonder if he had intentionally parked the mower on a slightly downhill slope. Little did I know at the time, but I was about to be inducted into an elite group of children who were given the duty of keeping the grass cut on our five acres of generously-wooded Indiana homestead. The annual induction ceremony consisted of a meeting held in the spring before the grass could get too high. Attendees were all the children in our family who were physically able to push a mower, and not yet mentally capable of coming up with a good rationale for why they were too old, busy, and/or sophisticated for such menial tasks. Fortunately, with twelve brothers and sisters, this typically resulted in a group of at least three or four fairly capable grass cutters. The older members of this group would operate the large riding tractor-mower, while the younger ones were generally relegated to handling the push mowers.

At the dining room table, the scene was one of excited anticipation of possible new territories to subdue. Cutters returning from the previous year had a pretty good idea of how this meeting was conducted. The first order of business was to sketch an aerial view of our five acres, including representations of any and all landmarks that would require trimming with the push mower after being passed by with the tractor-mower. This included items such as trees, boulders, fences, buildings, and such. Since an attempt was made to divide the grass cutting duties evenly among the qualified children, it was important that no mowable feature of the yard be omitted from the sketch.

The sketch was typically begun by the most enthusiastic child who was first to grab a clean piece of paper from the old pale green file cabinet drawer next to our mom's desk near the kitchen. I can still remember the grinding screech of the drawer opening and closing. It sounded very much like the opening of our old folding metal ironing board, which was something akin to the bloodcurdling shriek of a witch who's being boiled alike in hot oil.[1] This ominous sound basically served to call our meeting to order. The sketch began with a rectangular outline of our property, which was marked off by long, straight fences on the north and south sides. The other boundaries consisted of the country road on which we lived to the east, and our cousins' property to the west. The outline of our house was next, along with our grandparents' trailers, since they lived behind us. The fish pond, swimming pool, and horse barn were also filled in. Then began the task of representing all the trees, bushes, and other semi-permanent features of the yard.

Once the sketch was completed, the senior-most child would take the lead by informing us of what portion of the yard would be his or hers. Choosing his favorite symbol (i.e., asterisk, star, etc.), he would mark each feature of the yard to be under his or her mowing-dominion with this symbol, taking extreme care to leave plenty of mowing for the rest of us. This activity proceeded down the line with some inevitable haggling, until they passed the schematic to me with a domineering, "Here, you get what's left." My disappointment that all the good symbols had already been taken was quickly eclipsed by my outrage at having been left a bit more than an equal share. Fortunately, my older siblings were receptive to my appeal and a process of giving and taking, sort of like with trading cards, ensued.

What made things more interesting was that every mowable feature of the yard had a degree of difficulty and a kind of personality associated with it. Fence rows were generally considered to be one of the more nasty characters, along with large fir trees with low branches. "I'll give you the south fence row for Grandma McCarthy's yard, the Virgin Mary Shrine, and the propane tank" my brother offered me with a gleam in his eye. His self-serving expression automatically elicited my reaction, "No way! That fence row takes forever to cut." Back and forth we would go for several minutes.

We must have looked like commodities traders during a market rush, except we were only dealing in various grass clippings. Often the erasing and reassigning would become so extensive that it required a complete redrawing of the schematic to start over from scratch. After several minutes of this, we would eventually settle upon a fairly stable solution, which would promptly be posted on the refrigerator door with a magnet. This is where most of the important public documents of our family lived. Here it could be quickly referenced, and extended in case of disputes that tended to arise over the course of the summer. All-in-all, it was a whole lot of work. Why does grass have to grow so fast?

Couldn't the World Have Been Better Engineered?

We all notice things about the world that we wish were different. We perceive our environment in terms of affordances that we immediately classify as either good or bad. And some of these affordances appear to be very bad indeed. While an AK-47 automatic assault rifle may afford self-defense, it also affords the rapid murder of many innocent victims by a terrorist. So much depends on the intentions of the end user. But if we're honest, experience tells us that our initial classification of affordances can sometimes be shortsighted. Perhaps you didn't care for the taste of spinach or kale the first time you tried them. As children, we are tempted to conclude that green leafy vegetables afford nothing but a bitter, disagreeable taste in our mouths. But now as an adult, I grow lots of spinach and kale in my garden every year because I know they afford good health and can even be made into some very tasty dishes.

Adversity is another aspect of life that we wish we could avoid. Pain, fatigue, and discomfort all seem at first glance to be negative experiences. But pain is often an important signifier that something is wrong with our body, and needs our immediate attention. Thus, C. S. Lewis writes in his classic, *The Problem of Pain*, "Hence, even in a perfect world, the necessity for those danger signals which the pain-fibres in our nerves are apparently designed to transmit."[2] As an athlete, I have learned to distinguish the important difference between appropriate fatigue, discomfort, or even pain during intense training, and a more severe pain that indicates overtraining or the onset of serious injury.

But notice in the case of the athlete how an appropriate amount of adversity, accepted with a humble redemptive attitude,[3] affords improved strength and skill. The truth of the often-heard axiom of the gym, "No pain, no gain," has been confirmed many times over by its ardent practitioners. Perhaps this axiom is also true in a larger sense when it comes to the engineering of our spirits. It's no secret that the human condition is loaded with adversity. But could it be that a cosmic engineer is using this adversity in a redemptive environment to make us stronger and wiser? Many examples could be cited of how important truths are often learned in the midst of adversity.

One of the most important truths we must learn is who we really are as humans. What is our true nature? If we are being engineered by our Maker, and for our Maker, it could be that some of the adversity inherent in our world is intended to help us realize this vital truth. Lewis illustrates this well as he writes,

> pain . . . shatters the illusion that what we have, whether good or bad in itself, is our own and enough for us. Everyone has noticed how hard it is to turn our thoughts to God when everything is going well with us. We 'have all we want' is a terrible saying when 'all' does not include God . . . Now God, who has made us, knows what we are and that our happiness lies in Him. Yet we will not seek it in Him as long as He leaves us any other resort where it can even plausibly be looked for. While what we call 'our own life' remains agreeable we will not surrender it to Him. What then can God do in our interests but make 'our own life' less agreeable to us, and take away the plausible source of false happiness.[4]

Jeremiah 9:7 seems appropriate in this context, where the Maker says, "See, I will refine and test them, for what else can I do because of the sin of my people?" Apparently, adversity affords a kind of wake-up call to the most important aspects of reality.

But there is another reason why a Cosmic Engineer might allow us to experience a significant amount of adversity in this world. Religious philosopher Richard Swinburne points out that certain kinds of especially valuable free choice are possible only as responses to evil and adversity. "I can show courage in bearing my suffering only if I am suffering. I can show sympathy for you, and help you in various ways, only if you are suffering and need help."[5] Thus, adversity affords opportunities to grow in compassion, kindness, and love toward those in need. It also affords humility and wisdom as we recognize our human frailties and limitations, and respond appropriately. According to Christianity, these are examples of how the creation affords an invitation to a deeper relationship with our Maker. Augustine wrote, "God judged it better to bring good out of evil, than not to permit any evil to exist."[6] Certainly, such a brief approach does not answer all questions regarding adversity in the world, but these initial steps toward an answer seem reasonable, and should encourage further exploration into the veracity of a Christian worldview.

Claims of Substandard Engineering: What about Death?

As humans have become more skilled in technology, it's tempting for us to make judgmental pronouncements about how various aspects of the creation could have been better engineered. An example of how the human genome appears to occasionally "malfunction," resulting in disease, pain, and suffering, was discussed in Chapter Three. Others have cited the reverse wiring of the human eye, the susceptibility to injury of the human spine and knee joint, and difficulties with the appendix, wisdom teeth, and the male prostate gland as additional examples of substandard engineering, which would be unworthy of a creative deity. Scientist and author Jonathan Sarfati responds to such claims from a young-earth creationist perspective in Chapter Twelve (What about 'Poorly Designed' Things?) of his book *By Design: Evidence for Nature's Intelligent Designer—the God of the Bible*.[7]

Ultimately, arguments over poor design in nature are philosophical or theological discussions that suffer from inadequate human understanding of all the issues involved. In his book on engineering ethics, philosopher Brad Kallenberg writes, "Design reasoning does not produce a single, ideally correct answer to a given problem but rather generates a wide variety of rival solutions that vie with each other for their relative level of 'satisfactoriness.'"[8] Thus, for human-engineered systems, it is hard enough to determine the "best" design from the viable candidates. It is even harder to make this determination for natural systems when metaphysical issues are also in play. Even so, our diligent attempts to copy nature (hence the exploding field of biomimetics) speaks volumes of our admiration and appreciation for the excellence of natural systems.

When lists are made of engineering challenges for the next century, human "immortality" seems to always find a place near the top. Indeed, if the humble flatworm can virtually live forever (see the example of planaria in Chapter Nine), why not human beings? Death is commonly viewed as a great evil to be overcome, and over the years strides have been made to increase average human life expectancy. But the aging process in humans has stubbornly resisted all of our attempts at eradication or reversal. Of course, many people believe in some kind of afterlife, but why must we come face-to-face with the specter of physical death? Why would a cosmic engineer make us in such a way that our physical bodies end up just wasting away?

In his insightful article, "An Ecological Perspective on the Role of Death in Creation," biologist John Wood emphasizes the pervasiveness of death in vital ecological relationships. He writes, "Without the formative mechanism of mortality through which ecological processes occur, we cannot describe the shape, or the behavior, or the system functioning of the biosphere. Nothing in ecology makes sense apart from the operations of physical death."[9] His application of these ideas yield insights that enhance our stewardship of nature: First, physical death appears to have been present from the beginning, as a good part of God's gift of creation, and we should gratefully receive it.[10] Second, the fruitfulness of creation is necessarily balanced by endings. Third, a flourishing creation depends on a better understanding of death and dying. And fourth, death is a necessary correlate in the story of a free and contingent universe, although physical death is not the only story.[11] Theologian Paul Santmire writes, "But the final word of evolutionary biology always seems to come to this: death is the engine of nature."[12] With reference to Santmire, Wood concludes his article with, "Perhaps as the mystic Francis recognized nearly eight hundred years ago, ecologists are right to welcome 'sister death' as an integral part of creation's processes . . . if death is the engine of nature, then life is the fuel."[13]

If there is such a Cosmic Engineer, presumably humans stand as the crowning achievement. But many resist the notion of an engineered world because of the extent of pain and suffering associated with the human condition. Admittedly this is a major challenge, but human experience in general, and engineering research in particular, speak of the critical role that adversity and failure play in the acquisition of wisdom and the success of engineering design. Henry Petroski, author and professor of civil engineering and history at Duke University, investigates this concept in his book, *Success through Failure: the Paradox of Design*, where he writes, "Failure is thus a unifying principle in the design of things large and small, hard and soft, real and imagined . . . Whatever is being designed, success is achieved by properly anticipating and obviating failure."[14] Could the perceived failures in our lives actually be the avenues through which a Cosmic Engineer is successfully achieving his purposes?

Related to this is the idea that good engineers are often able to take something which appears to be bad and somehow "turn it around" and cause it to work for good. Sometimes this is referred to as "blessing in disguise" or "making the devil work for you." This concept is recognized as an important part of the inventive process of creative problem-solving as described in Semyon Savransky's book *Engineering of Creativity: Introduction to TRIZ Methodology of Inventive Problem Solving*. Converting harm into benefit is one of the forty inventive principles selected by Genrich Altshuller after an extensive study of thousands of patents from around the world.[15] Perhaps it is also an underlying theme that can help to explain the adversity associated with the human condition.

Christian theology resonates strongly with this perspective. Wood points out that "the metaphors of 'pruning,' of 'dying daily,' and of saying that 'unless a seed dies it abides alone' all seem to point to physical death as a normal end."[16] But I would take this a step further. These are images of a Cosmic Engineer who refines and redeems his creation through adversity and death. Lewis paints a clear picture of this by imagining a chess match between God and Satan. He writes,

> human Death is the result of sin and the triumph of Satan. But it is also the means of redemption from sin, God's medicine for Man and His weapon against Satan. In a general way, it is not difficult to understand how the same thing can be a masterstroke on the part of one combatant and also the very means whereby the superior combatant defeats him. Every good general, every good chess-player takes what is precisely the strong point of his opponent's plan and makes it the pivot of his own plan. Take that castle of mine if you insist. It was not

my original intention that you should—indeed, I thought you would have had more sense. But take it by all means. For now I move thus . . . and thus . . . and it is mate in three moves. Something like this must be supposed to have happened about Death.[17]

A Christian understanding of mortality offers an important distinction between physical death and spiritual death. Astronomer and apologist Hugh Ross highlights this distinction in his book, *Why the Universe Is the Way It Is*, where he writes,

From the moment spiritual death (autonomy from God) invaded creation, physical death became a blessing, an avenue through which God could temper the outbreak of evil and suffering. More importantly, through death—his own and that of human beings—the Creator could enact his plan of redemption . . . The universe with all its features, laws and dimensions represents the perfect theatre for enactment of God's redemptive drama. By its physical constraints, God limits the spread of evil, encourages the pursuit of virtue, and demonstrates his great love for humankind. According to the Bible, this temporal universe provides an essential proving ground to test each human heart (in the spiritual sense) and prepare those who pass the test for life in a completely new realm, one that includes all the features we long for and more—the perfection we can barely imagine.[18]

In short, death affords the possibility of redemption and ultimate fulfillment in a way that humans can only partially comprehend.[19]

Why Would a Maker Paint Nature Red in Tooth and Claw?

Scientists, engineers, philosophers, and theologians all have a part to play in helping us understand the implications of the affordance-laden, yet often disturbing, structures of our universe. Physicist and atheist Sean Carrol admits that "Given a conventional understanding of what is meant by 'God,' the fact that the universe exhibits regularities at all, and in particular that it exhibits regularities that allow for the existence of human beings, has a higher likelihood under theism than naturalism."[20] But he has adopted a worldview he calls "poetic naturalism," claiming that humans can construct goodness by coming up with their own, more flexible, moral code.[21] Others reject the idea of a benevolent cosmic engineer because they see it as inconsistent with long ages of suffering and death associated with the evolutionary story of life's history.

Theologian Bethany Sollereder points out in her excellent article, "Evolution, Suffering, and the Creative Love of God," that "Quite apart from the necessity for physical regularity, many of the aspects of life that we find so deeply disturbing actually provide necessary functions without which life would be impossible. They are 'package deals.'"[22] As an example, she discusses an aspect of geology known as plate tectonics, in which massive parts of the earth's crust collide, causing earthquakes, tsunamis, and volcanic activity. Normally, the ground below our feet affords standing, walking, and stability for all living creatures, but occasionally it undulates with unpredictable and alarming amplitudes that often afford destruction, injury, and death. But she cites three ways that scientific investigation has shown that these destructive processes are also instrumental in renewing the earth and "absolutely necessary to life."[23]

First, the active recycling of carbon dioxide into the atmosphere through plate subduction (one plate sliding under another) affords a stable temperature and the primary necessity for life: liquid surface water. Second, the released greenhouse gases, such as carbon dioxide, are then trapped near the earth's surface, allowing the planet to retain heat while Earth's magnetic field wards off potentially lethal doses of cosmic radiation and solar wind that would slowly strip away our atmosphere. Thus, we are afforded an important protective shield by the same processes that drive plate movement. Finally, the processes of plate tectonics help to afford a stable surface temperature by using up heat produced by the earth's radioactive core and mantle.[24] This example illustrates how certain aspects of our planet that were long-thought to be negative toward life are now understood to be essential for life.

Sollereder also addresses the challenging issue of pain and suffering during long periods of biological evolution. What about the multitudes of animals whose lives are cut off in infancy before they had any chance to flourish and whose experience of life is predominated by pain, suffering, and neglect?[25] Who is to blame? As John Polkinghorne has argued, God, through an act of love, made the world with free process, which also means that not every result of the process is the result of divine engineering.[26] "Yet, even with the acknowledgement of great freedom, it still seems that a heavy weight of responsibility for the suffering that results from evolution rests on God."[27]

But consider the key relationships that exist in nature that afford things of value. "It is the very competitiveness and strife of the evolutionary process that pressures it into such wonderful creativity. Many of the values of creation are directly attributable to the harms that cause them to arise."[28] The cougar's fang affords the elegance and speed of the deer. Theologian Christopher Southgate has suggested that evolution involving pain and predation may be the only way to develop creaturely individuals in a physical environment without continual divine intervention.[29] Thus, in producing novel and complex creatures via these relationships, the world appears to exhibit, at least on the surface, a significant level of autonomy. Southgate pushes the argument further to say that evolution is not only the best means for filling the earth, but perhaps also the only way to afford beings that will one day populate heaven.[30] In this giving of freedom and autonomy to creation, Sollereder sees something of the creativity and respect of love in the evolutionary narrative, since love, by its very nature, will not control the beloved.[31]

In concluding her article, Sollereder suggests that God responds to suffering in three ways: companioning, luring, and redeeming. Comparing the Creator to a dedicated midwife, or even a laboring mother, she writes, "In every instance, God is with each creature: inspiring its every breath, constantly giving it the power to be, and accompanying it through life. This means that whenever any creature suffers, God suffers with it, feeling the full extent of its pain."[32] In addition, God is active in influencing the outcomes of creation, luring all entities toward good and harmonious relationships. The lure of God toward life means that creatures will continually become more complex and that the interrelationships between life forms will become more complex.[33] It also means that all animal suffering will be drawn toward good ends.

Finally, an immediate redemption is accomplished simply because of the way ecosystems work. In the continuous exchange of life and death, the death of a creature is never wasted.[34] "Most of the lives cut short are brought to an end because they are eaten by something else—the lives lost are directly involved in the flourishing of another. Even when they are not directly eaten, the energy and materials stored in their bodies are eventually recycled and reused by other organisms."[35] Furthermore, a delayed redemption is envisioned by those who suggest that animals that never had a chance to flourish will be redeemed by a new life in heaven where they will be able to experience both the goodness of Earth and the greatness of God.[36]

Sollereder proposes a third model of redemption that combines the insights of both the immediate and delayed models into a dual-aspect redemption.[37] She suggests that the story of each creature, both in its flourishing and in its suffering, is combined with all the other narratives of creation in such a way as to make an overarching narrative that reflects back to the glory and honor of the individual, and ultimately on the Maker. The image she suggests for visualizing this idea is the photo mosaic, which is basically a big picture made up of a combination of carefully chosen smaller pictures. See Figure 10–1 below for an example of this innovative type of artistry.[38]

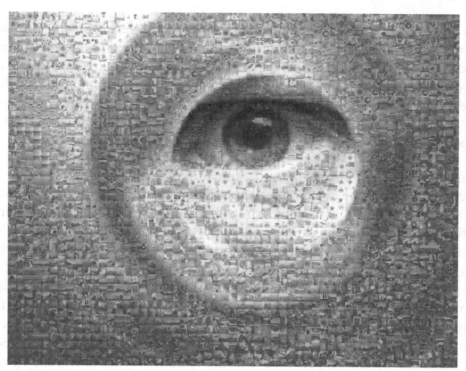

Figure 10–1   Example of a Photo Mosaic
© Shutterstock.com

Our lives and the lives of all living creatures are like those smaller pictures. Each is a whole story in itself, unique and necessary. But God arranges the stories next to each other, in both space and time, in order to bring out larger redemptive patterns: an image of universal harmony in multiple dimensions. Furthermore, this creation is not limited to just two levels, as shown in the figure. Each smaller picture could itself be a mosaic, and each pixel of that smaller picture a mosaic also, and so on.[39] This is what philosopher Eleonore Stump calls "nested fractal narratives,"[40] and it is basically an illustration of nested affordances.

According to Sollereder,

the photo mosaic of nested fractal narratives holds together two major theological emphases: freedom and meaning . . . Creatures build their own life stories in freedom, with their own meaning in light of their environments and relationships, but the final arrangement of those pieces in the great mosaic of redemption comes from God. That great picture will pick up the photographs that creatures have made with their lives—and is thus responsive to the freedom of creation—but it will also arrange them in a new and unforeseen pattern, making new and positive meanings out of old, and sometimes extremely negative events.[41]

Through divine companioning, lure, and redemption, "God acts in perfect love. What that looks like in practice, however, will be as unique as the creature who is loved."[42] This image provides a powerful illustration of how a loving Mastermind may be causing *all* things to work together for good.[43]

STEWARDSHIP IN ADVERSITY AFFORDS WISDOM AND MATURITY

From an early age, we learned that the process of "subduing the earth" is facilitated by planning, cooperation, teamwork, and creativity. We learned many such lessons growing up in a big family. We learned that good stewardship can be hard work but it pays off in the end. We enjoyed playing football, and baseball, and even golf, on the grassy areas of our yard which were carefully kept cut. Sometimes the mowers were used to cuts field lines, base paths, and putting greens, which significantly enhanced the athletic experience. I remember when one of my older brothers showed me how to plant a tin can flush in the ground to serve as a golf hole. There was no more beautiful sound than my golf ball hitting the bottom of that can. It was the exact opposite of the sounds my golf ball made when it hit Grandma's trailer on one occasion, and the side of our garage on another. I still had a few lessons left to learn about golf and stewardship.

STUDY QUESTIONS

1. Describe your first job and the impact it had on your life. Are you grateful for the experience? Why or why not?
2. How might the axiom "No pain, no gain" apply to the engineering of the human spirit?
3. How does pain and adversity "wake us up" to the most important aspects of reality?
4. What kind of important opportunities does adversity bring? What do we gain by responding positively to these opportunities?
5. Do you find arguments that the human body is a poor example of design compelling? Why or why not?
6. According to Wood, how should we view physical death, and how does this impact our handling of nature?
7. How could failure be an integral part of a successful design? Could this idea lend insight into the human condition?
8. What insight does C. S. Lewis provide concerning death?
9. How does the distinction between physical death and spiritual death inform our understanding of the redemptive aspects of nature?
10. What does Sollereder mean when she claims that adversity and life are "package deals"?
11. Describe the ways in which God responds to suffering in the world.
12. How does the idea of a photo mosaic provide a picture of God's action in the world?

ENDNOTES

1. Or so claims comedian Brian Regan.

2. C. S. Lewis, *The Problem of Pain* (London: Collins, 1940), 23.

3. To strive for improvement, one must first admit a certain level of inadequacy.

4. Lewis, *Problem of Pain*, 94.

5. Richard Swinburne, *The Existence of God* (New York: Oxford University Press, 2004), 241.

6. Saint Augustine, *The Enchiridion On Faith, Hope and Love* (London: Aeterna Press, 2014), 18.

7. Jonathan Sarfati, *By Design: Evidence for Nature's Intelligent Designer—the God of the Bible* (Atlanta, GA: Creation Ministries International, 2008), 191–218.

8. Brad Kallenberg, *By Design: Ethics, Theology and the Practice of Engineering* (Cambridge: James Clark and Company, 2013), back cover.

9. John R. Wood, "An Ecological Perspective on the Role of Death in Creation," *Perspectives on Science and Christian Faith* 68, no. 2 (June 2016): 77–78.

10. The fossil record indicates that physical death existed long before the fall of mankind, which was primarily marked by spiritual death, or separation from God.

11. Wood, "An Ecological Perspective," 80–81.

12. H. Paul Santmire, *Nature Reborn: The Ecological and Cosmic Promise of Christian Theology* (Minneapolis, MN: Augsburg Fortress, 2000), 94.

13. Wood, "An Ecological Perspective," 82.

14. Henry Petroski, *Success through Failure: The Paradox of Design* (Princeton, NJ: Princeton University Press, 2006), 5.

15. Semyon Savransky, *Engineering of Creativity: Introduction to TRIZ Methodology of Inventive Problem Solving* (Boca Raton, FL: CRC Press, 2000), 212.

16. Wood, "An Ecological Perspective," 81.

17. C. S. Lewis, *Miracles* (London: Collins, 1947), 208–09.

18. Hugh Ross, *Why the Universe Is the Way It Is* (Grand Rapids, MI: Baker Books, 2008), 150–51.

19. According to 1 Corinthians 2:9, "What no eye has seen, what no ear has heard, and what no human mind has conceived"—the things God has prepared for those who love him.

20. Sean Carroll, *The Big Picture: On the Origins of Life, Meaning, and the Universe Itself* (New York: Dutton, 2016), 196.

21. Carroll, *The Big Picture*, 412–18.

22. Bethany Sollereder, "Evolution, Suffering, and the Creative Love of God," *Perspectives on Science and Christian Faith* 68, no. 2 (June 2016): 100.

23. Sollereder, "Evolution, Suffering, and the Creative Love of God," 100.

24. Sollereder, "Evolution, Suffering, and the Creative Love of God," 100.

25. Christopher Southgate, *The Groaning of Creation: God, Evolution and the Problem of Evil* (Louisville, KY: Westminster John Knox Press, 2008), 48–50.

26. John Polkinghorne, *Science and Providence: God's Interaction with the World* (West Conshohocken, PA: Templeton Foundation Press, 1989), 77.

27. Sollereder, "Evolution, Suffering, and the Creative Love of God," 104.

28. Sollereder, "Evolution, Suffering, and the Creative Love of God," 103.

29. Southgate, *Groaning of Creation*, 29.

30. Southgate, *Groaning of Creation*, 90.

31. W. H. Vanstone, *Love's Endeavor, Love's Expense: The Response of Being to the Love of God* (London: Darton, Longman and Todd, 1977), 45–49. And more recently, Thomas J. Oord, *The Uncontrolling Love of God: An Open and Relational Account of Providence* (Downers Grove, IL: InterVarsity, 2015).

32. Sollereder, "Evolution, Suffering, and the Creative Love of God," 104.

33. Sollereder, "Evolution, Suffering, and the Creative Love of God," 104–05. At this point in the article, she also explicitly describes one of the hierarchical nested affordance structures we have been discussing, "It is the pattern that we have seen throughout evolutionary history: prokaryotic cells become eukaryotic, single-celled organisms join colonies, colonies become multicellular organisms, organisms specialize into diverse and complex organisms, which in turn promote complex ecological relations. Even when cataclysmic devastations threaten to wipe out life on Earth, each time life has bounced back and displayed even more diversity and complexity than before."

34. Holmes Rolston III, "Does Nature Need to be Redeemed?" *Zygon* 29, no. 2 (June 1994): 205–29.

35. Sollereder, "Evolution, Suffering, and the Creative Love of God," 105.

36. Jay B. McDaniel, *Of Gods and Pelicans: A Theology of Reverence for Life* (Louisville, KY: Westminster John Knox, 1989), 19–21.

37. Sollereder, "Evolution, Suffering, and the Creative Love of God," 106.

38. Looking at this combination of small pictures from sufficiently far away should result in the emergence of a human eye as the overarching big picture. This big picture is easily missed by looking at the figure too closely.

39. Sollereder, "Evolution, Suffering, and the Creative Love of God," 106.

40. Eleonore Stump, *Wandering in Darkness: Narrative and the Problem of Suffering* (Oxford: Clarendon, 2010), 219–26, 466–67.

41. Sollereder, "Evolution, Suffering, and the Creative Love of God," 106.

42. Sollereder, "Evolution, Suffering, and the Creative Love of God," 107.

43. Romans 8:28.

CHAPTER ELEVEN

Wisdom and Love Expressed by Affordances That Invite Relationship

LOVE FROM ABOVE

Being the eleventh of thirteen children, I only knew my dad in his later years, when he usually seemed to be a rather serious man. But every once in a while, the playfulness of his youth would break forth with unexpected delight. I knew he was a bit of a "cut-up" in his younger days because I remember when I was very little coming across various props for practical jokes while searching through his dresser drawers. I don't remember why I was searching through the sock drawer in my parents' bedroom, but I was quite surprised to uncover a dribble cup, a rubber fried egg, a fake hypodermic needle, and a very lifelike rubber hand, among other things. I had fallen prey to the rubber egg a year or so earlier, discovering the truth only after a vigorous attack with my fork was turned back.

Most of the time, however, Dad seemed concerned that we would develop an admirable work ethic. In fact, some of my older brothers used to call him "Mr. Work." One brother in particular (who shall remain nameless) would vex Dad terribly by dragging himself out of bed on a Saturday morning in response to Dad's call, only to relocate and resume his slumber in some unexpected place like the front door closet. These episodes did not put Dad in a happy mood. Rarely did I see my dad act in a playful manner, but when he did, he made the most of it.

There were a couple of occasions when he made use of his airplane piloting skills to express his love for us in an unusual, but very effective, manner. The first involved an ill-prepared float trip down the Wildcat Creek. We were blessed to have a fairly good-sized creek winding its way through the countryside only a couple miles from our home. My brothers enjoyed biking to the creek to go fishing, and often returned home with good-sized catfish, desperately clinging to life as they dangled from the bicycle handlebars. Sometimes my brothers would immediately throw them in the pond behind our house, in hopes of stocking it with fish. On other occasions they would present their catch to Mom in hopes of receiving a catfish dinner for their efforts.

On very special occasions, we kids would head to the creek for an all-day float trip, taking along inner tubes, canoes, and our flat bottom boat, which usually rested on the banks of our pond. One of the first such trips that I can recall turned out to be a long, hot summer day when our provisions ran short. The food we had brought did not last us nearly long enough. Dad and Mom must have noticed our meager preparations as we left that morning, because they came to our rescue in grand fashion. That afternoon, as we lay famished on a sandbar with the boats temporarily pulled ashore, and desperately wishing we had something to eat, we heard a small sound. It was the familiar sound of an airplane, which immediately drew our attention since we were all oriented toward aviation, having basically grown up on an airport owned by my Dad and his two brothers.

"That sounds like a Cessna 172" said one of my brothers, eager to demonstrate his intimate knowledge of aircraft. Any time an airplane was spotted in the sky, or just simply heard, the game of "who could identify it first" began. As we stood on the sandbar and scanned the patches of sky clear of the trees that lined the banks of the creek, the engine noise got louder. Presently, the unusually low flying airplane came into full view, and was immediately recognized by the older brothers as Dad's 172. It was so low we could see Mom waving out of the passenger side window. This contact from home in our destitute state was quite rejuvenating. The plane "buzzed" us and circled back around as we jumped up and down and shouted various expressions of recognition and greeting which had no chance of being heard by our visitors above. Much to our amazement and delight, on the next trip by, Mom passed a large package wrapped in red plastic out the window, and bombed us with it! It sailed toward us with a long plastic tail flapping in the wind. Because of the wonder and joy of that moment, I still remember that sound vividly, and catch myself smiling whenever I hear the sound of plastic flapping in a breeze. It was a great shot by my Mom, and the "care package" landed in the middle of the creek about 50 feet from us.

At that moment we all ran across the sand bar and jumped in the creek, swimming like mad for the package. I don't remember who got there first, but we all helped to rip the package open and found the contents of peanut butter and jelly sandwiches to be extremely satisfying. Needless to say, we finished the trip with a bit more energy and enthusiasm. That float trip became one of the highlights of my childhood. The delivery of that care package did more than satisfy our hunger that afternoon. It confirmed to us that our parents loved us and cared for us, even when we acted stupidly by being ill-prepared and making poor choices. In particular, it communicated to us that our dad was willing to stop working and thrill us with an unexpected blessing, even at the expense of aircraft time and fuel cost. Many years later, when I was away at Purdue University, just across the Wabash River from the town where I grew up, I had a similar experience. But the rest of that story will have to wait until the end of this chapter.

Affordances Communicate Intentions and Emotions

In today's world, most professional engineers are hired by industry in order to create affordances associated with a particular product (i.e., a cell phone) that will turn a profit in the marketplace. Our commercial environment repeatedly communicates to us that engineered affordances that improve our lives are obtained at a price. To the savvy consumer, the overarching message is that engineering services and the resulting products are offered because someone is trying to make money. Thus, the primary intentions of the typical engineer would be those inherently bound up in capitalism (to earn a living doing meaningful work). And any emotions of the engineer and associated company (aside from suspected greed at being overcharged) would typically be lost in the exchange. Now, I think capitalism and free markets are an admirable and effective means of supporting an economy, but they can result in a somewhat cynical view of engineers and the affordances they produce. If all they care about is making money, then something very valuable has been lost.

As a result, people lose sight of the fact that engineers (and other creative agents) can communicate many things (especially intentions and emotions) through the affordances they create and provide to others. Even when gifts are given to communicate noble sentiments, they are often purchased, with minimal time and effort expended by the giver. Rarely are items handmade anymore, which would make for an even more meaningful and powerful gesture, since personal time, energy, and skill were invested. This sentiment was communicated effectively by Keith Hathaway (a.k.a. The Mad Hatter, or just "Hat" for short), one of my best friends from college who was also an engineer, when Kate and I had our first child. Unbeknownst to us, he had spent weeks designing and building a large wooden toy box with a latching lid that was beautifully crafted and finished. We were stunned and overwhelmed with a deep sense of gratitude when he presented it to us. If you've ever had someone create something for you like that, you know the kind of warm feelings it generates.

Each of our four children enjoyed digging through that huge toy box, and it has served us well for more than thirty years. We fondly remember Hat whenever we use it, because it reminds us of what he communicated to us through that simple affordance he had created just for us. It spoke of his desire that our children would be happy and that their many toys would be well-organized. It spoke of his love for our family and his intention to support and encourage us as our family grew. It also spoke of his willingness to use his talents and hard-earned personal resources for our benefit. Our acts of accepting his gift with thankful hearts and using it every day communicated our appreciation for his friendship and sacrifice.

Returning to the earlier example, my dad's relationship and skill with aircraft afforded him an opportunity to communicate his love for us kids when we were in need. He and my mom also displayed wisdom in how they delivered our surprise lunch. First of all, they were able to find us by flying along the path of the creek. Then, being a former barnstormer, Dad was daring enough to fly low so that my mom could accurately bomb us with the lunch package without getting it caught in a tree. She had also wrapped it tightly with plastic so the sandwiches wouldn't be ruined by nasty creek water. All this skill and wisdom was wrapped up in joviality and love to afford us with much needed sustenance, along with the unspoken reminder that our parents deeply cared for us.

Now let's apply these same concepts to the realm of nature. I have argued previously that nested affordances on display at all levels of the cosmos give us good reason to believe that the systems that comprise the universe, including our very lives, have been personally engineered for our benefit. If this is indeed the case, what intentions, attributes, and emotions might be communicated by such a rich landscape of affordances? Philosophers Erik Rietveld and Julian Kiverstein argue that "the affordances an environment offers to an animal are dependent on the skills the animal possesses. By virtue of our many abilities, the landscape of affordances we inhabit as humans is very rich and resourceful."[1] At the most fundamental level, this vast array of affordances plays a key role in allowing us to perceive reality; to know what is true. This is vital for our well-being, and indeed, our very survival.

For example, Rietveld and Kiverstein discuss the importance of recognizing constraints on human activity, such as a cliff edge, which does not afford locomotion. "The affordance of correctly naming this part of a landscape 'a cliff' is an obvious example that has normativity at its core. For philosophers this kind of affordance is important because seeing and/or stating correctly how things really are is fundamental to knowledge acquisition . . . We can say that things afford perceiving what they really are."[2] So, at the most basic level, our Maker intends for us to acquire knowledge and know truth. First and foremost, the universe appears to be engineered for this very purpose. There are some vital implications to this idea that will be pursued further in a later section.

It appears also that our Maker intends that we not only live, but that we generally enjoy life on this earth. All those things we appreciate in our lives were engineered by our Creator. Even the very capacity to enjoy those things was built into us by our Maker. Of course, there are negative aspects to the human condition, as has been discussed earlier, but on the whole, life is good. Consider the amazing diversity of people, places, and things that afford so much gratification. The earth affords a wonderful array of food and drink that keeps us healthy while simultaneously filling our senses with pleasurable tastes and aromas. The apostle Paul saw this as evidence of God's kindness toward us, as he described to the people of Lystra, "Yet he has not left himself without testimony: He has shown kindness by giving you rain from heaven and crops in their seasons; he provides you with plenty of food and fills your hearts with joy" (Acts 14:17). Even if our current human state was achieved through a process of mutation and natural selection, all this provision, in terms of the many affordances that we enjoy, is an indication of the Maker's generosity and love for us.

The incredible enormity of the matter and energy that sprang forth at the moment of the Big Bang (estimated at 4×10^{69} Joules[3]) points to an extremely powerful, perhaps omnipotent, Agent who is able to deal out energy in amounts that are impossible for us to even fathom. Considering also that the entire universe appears to have come from somewhere else, or even out of nothing, continues to confirm the complete "otherness" of this Maker. Astronomer and apologist Hugh Ross provides a helpful picture of a Creator who operates in dimensions beyond those of the cosmos in which we reside.[4] Paul attests to the universal evidential power of nature in his letter to the Romans. "For since the creation of the world God's invisible qualities—his eternal power and divine nature—have been clearly seen, being understood from what has been made, so that people are without excuse" (Romans 1:20).

The vast intelligence, wisdom, and ingenuity of our Maker are also communicated by the way innumerable affordances arise from the creation to meet our needs and desires. Human engineers know from experience that in the simplest case, the number of layers in a series of nested affordances corresponds to the number of relationships that are being arranged to produce an ultimate affordance for the end-user. The situation only becomes more complicated when multiple relationships are involved at a particular level, or multiple interdependencies exist between various affordances at various levels. Nature exhibits this kind of super-complexity at many different levels, but especially when it comes to living systems. Scientists have worked diligently for centuries, but due to the level of complexity, nature is stingy in revealing her secrets. For example, we still don't understand much about the workings of the human brain. Yet, it is generally agreed that our brains are a masterpiece of engineering, with connections and layers of affordances that seem to surpass our ability to comprehend. It is reasonable to conclude that all these affordances are somehow planned, arranged, and sustained by the wisdom and ingenuity of our unseen Maker.

But even though our Creator is far above and beyond us in so many ways, Christian tradition maintains that we are made in the image of our Maker; that we were made to be spiritual, moral, rational, and relational beings; creatures that are capable of entering into an intimate relationship with our Creator. As described in Psalm 19, the realm of nature declares the glory of the Maker. The affordances of the universe speak of God's power and divinity; his intelligence, wisdom, and ingenuity; his creativity and resourcefulness; his desire for us to know truth; and his generosity and love for his creatures. I think he also wants us to have fun. I like to remind people that God made us for the fun of it. And he invites us to join in his fun. The next section explores how affordances also play a key role in inviting us to the party.

Affordances Invite Behavior and Relationship

As was briefly mentioned in Chapter Six, recent studies in ecological psychology recognize that affordances can prompt certain behaviors by agents (animals or people). The determining factors and conditions that influence these phenomena are current areas of research. This branch of psychology helps us understand why we behave the way we do. Psychologist James Gibson's foundational work in affordances was largely in response to a mechanistic view in which agents respond to their environment in ways that are determined by the environment. While he acknowledged that behavior is certainly influenced by environmental affordances, he argued that agents choose between a multitude of perceived affordances based on the situation. In other words, affordances are "equally a fact of the environment and a fact of behavior."[5]

Psychologist Edward Reed built on Gibson's work, focusing on the "intentions" that agents form. "From an ecological point of view, intentions are not causes of action, but patterns of organization of action; they are not mental as opposed to physical . . . they are spread out across mind, body, information, ecological context, and social setting."[6] He developed the idea of "perception-action cycles"[7] to describe how agents organize information in choosing between competing affordances. This has led to the study of how affordances can invite certain actions, and why agents find some affordances more inviting than others.

Psychologist Rob Withagen and his research team have presented several factors that influence the attractiveness of a particular affordance. They suggest that these invitations depend on the agent-environment relationship in multiple dimensions.[8] These factors emanate from the concerns and capabilities of the agent. What actions is a particular agent physically, mentally, or emotionally capable of accomplishing? And how much effort needs to be expended in each of these areas? As Mark Twain famously quipped, "The person who does not read has no advantage over the one who cannot read." Perhaps people don't choose this affordance because they find reading too mentally taxing and time-consuming.

Besides the capabilities of the agent, another factor that bears on the invitational nature of a particular affordance is its importance for the agent's survival and flourishing. High on the priority list of a typical agent are the twin concerns of staying alive and reproducing. Hence, affordances that fall in line with these concerns are generally found to be very attractive. An agent's social conditioning, personal history, and individual experiences also help to determine the various degrees of attraction to affordances.[9] Ultimately, we are strongly attracted to affordances that satisfy fundamental urges and contribute to our survival, but these attractions will be somewhat modified by our own story, and these modifications will depend largely on the community in which we were raised.

Many nested affordances seem to converge toward the goal of human survival, but not all scientists see this as evidence for a cosmic engineer. Physicist Neil deGrasse Tyson has recently suggested that if there is a God out there somewhere, the inhospitable nature of the universe and the many physical dangers associated with life on earth indicate that this God is out to kill you![10] That may be one way to interpret the evidence, but upon further thought, this seems to be a somewhat superficial reading of our cosmological situation. First of all, why would God go to all the trouble of creating us and providing for us so bountifully and beautifully if all he wants to do is kill us off? Is he just the ultimate cosmic sadist, similar to a mean little kid who is scanning the sidewalk for the next bug he can squash? Doesn't the average human lifespan of about seventy-two years (as of 2016)[11] suggest otherwise?

Perhaps the magnificent oasis that is planet Earth is one way that God expresses his love and care for us by setting it against the harsh backdrop of outer space. In addition, dangers and hardships provide us with opportunities to grow in love and compassion for others. But more importantly, perhaps he's trying to communicate to us that this finite physical life is not that important, relative to an eternal spiritual life. If death is just a transition, not a termination, then the end of our earthly lives is not the great evil that it is often assumed to be. It all depends on our perspective. If we recognize that our lives have indeed been engineered for the purpose of knowing our Maker, then actually meeting our Maker face-to-face, according to his timing, should be an immense joy, and the start of a new and incredible adventure.

Engineered to Pursue Relationships

The laws of nature and the layout of the universe appear to be engineered for the purpose of inviting us, and encouraging us, into a relationship with our Maker, and discouraging us from a tendency toward isolation. The more progress we make in the behavioral sciences, the more we are beginning to realize that humans are made to be in deep and significant relationships. Psychiatrist Robert Waldinger is the fourth director of the Harvard Study of Adult Development, which is perhaps the longest in-depth study of adult life that has ever been done. For seventy-five years this study tracked the lives of 724 men in an effort to answer the question, "What keeps us healthy and happy as we go through life?" Waldinger summarized the fascinating findings of this extremely rare longitudinal study in a recent TED talk.[12]

According to Waldinger, "The clearest message we get from this 75-year study is this: Good relationships keep us happier and healthier. Period."[13] And three big lessons were learned about these relationships: First, social connections are really good for us and loneliness kills. It turns out that people who are more socially connected to family, friends, and community are happier, healthier, and they live longer than people who are less well connected. Second, it's not just the number of friends you have, or whether or not you're in a committed relationship, but it's the quality of your close relationships that matters. Third, good relationships don't just protect our bodies, they protect our brains, memories, and clarity of thought. Throughout the length of the study, the people who fared the best were those who "leaned into their relationships."[14]

Waldinger also gave some practical suggestions for what it means to "lean into" a relationship. Ultimately, it entails the (often) hard work of loving and caring for the other person in ways that communicate your deep commitment to the quality and longevity of the relationship. In many respects, the study was a confirmation of the primacy of love for human health and happiness. We are usually free to choose many of our important relationships, such as close friendships and marriage. However, we find ourselves born into other key relationships, as with parents, siblings, and other relatives.[15]

But there is one more relationship that we fortunately stumble into simply by being born into this world. Through the providence of creation, God communicates our sacred standing as his creatures, and offers us redemption and adoption into his family, culminating in a marriage-like relationship, as we are prepared to be the bride of Christ. Jesus emphasized the preeminence of this ultimate relationship by reminding us that the most important thing is to love our Maker with our whole being. And then to love others as we love ourselves.[16] The Harvard Study of Adult Development confirms the vital importance of tending to the crucial relationships in our lives. If the first and foremost of these is the relationship with our Maker, then we dare not reject, or neglect, such a magnanimous offer of amazing love. Perhaps the dire consequences of pursing isolationist policies in this life are indicative of the eventual separation from God that results from rejecting his offer. Even so, the creation seems to be engineered to gently tutor us in this regard, as described in the next section.

Consequences of Natural Laws as Signifiers

In the previous chapter, it was noted that physical pain is often an important indicator, or signifier, that something is wrong with our bodies and needs our attention. Recall from Chapter Four that Donald Norman, in his book *The Design of Everyday Things*, introduces the idea of a signifier as a feature engineers build into a product to help communicate the purpose, structure, or operation of the device to the user. In other words, a signifier is any perceivable indicator that helps a person know how to behave. A windsock was offered as an example of an engineered device that signifies the amount of wind, allowing pilots to decide if a flight in current conditions would be wise. And it was suggested that our universal internal sense of right and wrong also serves as a kind of signifier of appropriate behavior. People all around the world generally have the same ideas about right and wrong. And this instinctive sense of ethics tends to guide their behavior. When we act wrongly, we experience guilt and shame. And when we heed the advice of the angel on our shoulder, we tend to experience the opposite; satisfaction and even fulfillment, as if we are living in a way which accords with our purpose.

In his classic book, *Mere Christianity*, C. S. Lewis referred to this sense of right and wrong as a clue to the meaning of the universe.[17] Recall from Chapter Seven that reverse engineers search for any pertinent clues to help them understand the meaning and purpose of the system they are studying. Donald Norman's signifiers, even when discovered in natural systems, are revealing of meaning and purpose in nature. The presence of signifiers is another indication that the universe is an engineered system, with a cosmic engineer who desires to communicate with his creatures about what behavior is in their best interest.

Astrophysicist and Christian apologist Hugh Ross describes the interesting consequential nature of physical laws in his book, *Why the Universe Is the Way It Is*. Referring to the Genesis account of the curse resulting from the Fall,[18] he writes, "God's pronouncements on Adam and Eve and the ground were not only a judgment but also a warning. When humans practice evil, they experience additional pain and work . . . No one enjoys seeing time wasted or being stuck with extra work or pain. The desire to avoid hardship is strong in every individual. This trait is so strong that parents, teachers, military officers, and governing authorities use extra work, pain, and wasted time as tools to correct unacceptable behavior. Evidently, God designed the laws of physics so that the more depraved people become the worse consequences they suffer . . . Physical laws not only discourage expression of harmful impulses but also encourage good behavior."[19] He goes on to provide a few examples of such good and bad consequences that tend to encourage and discourage, respectively, the type of behavior for which we were engineered.

One example that quickly comes to mind is the way my particularly selfish behavior will rapidly alienate me from others and tend to torpedo my close relationships. On the other hand, if I "lean into" my relationships by working hard at expressing my love for others, especially in their particular "love language,"[20] relationships are enhanced and satisfaction and fulfillment ensue. Jesus painted a powerful word picture that beautifully illustrates this concept in what may be the most well-known story ever told: The parable of the Prodigal Son.[21] It seems clear from this story that the selfish behavior of the son, though initially making him quite popular with some people, quickly led to his alienation and frustration as he wallowed in the pigpen. But his adverse condition turned out to work for his good as he soon realized that his best course of action was to return home and seek forgiveness for his selfish and foolish behavior. Unfortunately, I have firsthand experience with this kind of behavior, as revealed in the following account from my college days.

MORE LOVE FROM ABOVE

The second time my dad showered me with an uncommon blessing from above was during my rebellious college days at Purdue University. I was living in a wild and crazy co-op house near campus and trying to enjoy my newfound independence from home via several unhealthy and detrimental activities which are common among college students. On one particular Saturday afternoon, I was at a home football game at the Purdue Stadium, in a fairly inebriated state, but cognizant enough to hear one of my friends say, "Hey Dominic, is that message for you?" I turned to see that they were pointing up in the sky at an airplane that was pulling a string of red letters. This was an old-fashioned kind of banner that was painstakingly assembled, letter by letter on the runway, and typically used for rather expensive advertising. My dad operated this kind of banner business, and it was not unusual to see banners displaying various slogans and invitations to visit local establishments. However, it was extremely unusual to see a banner that read "HI DOMINIC," but that is exactly what this banner displayed.

Although there were probably many Dominics in the crowd of about 30,000 people at Ross Ade Stadium that day, I immediately knew that my dad was saying hi to me personally and expressing his love for me in a very extravagant way. I remember feeling overwhelmed and kind of embarrassed that out of all the huge crowd there, that banner message was just for me. In addition, I was struck by the fact that my dad was expressing his unconditional love for me at significant expense, while I was in the midst of a time of rebellion against the way of life he had recommended to me. This little message, a simple greeting, though presented at quite some cost, had little impact on my lifestyle at the time. But it served as a reminder of a nagging truth that ran in opposition to my current life direction.

That truth was the existence of unconditional love for me in my miserable state, and the existence of a better way of life. I think that if the father of the prodigal son in the Bible had owned a banner flying business, he would have sent a high-flying greeting of love to his pig-slopping son. But isn't this the same message that the father sent by running to the prodigal son while he was still a long way off and greeting him with a joyful hug? And isn't it the same message of love and acceptance that our heavenly Father communicates to each one of us through his fabulous provision found in nature and his wonderful redemption found in the sacrifice of his Son?

STUDY QUESTIONS

1. Describe a time when you received a significant and undeserved act of kindness. How did it affect you?
2. Describe some things that engineers can communicate through the affordances they create for others.
3. What are some fundamental truths that are communicated through the affordances present in nature?
4. What characteristics of our Maker are communicated through affordances and other features of the universe?
5. What determines how agents choose between competing affordances?
6. Suggest some responses to Tyson's claims that the universe is too dangerous to be the work of a caring Maker.
7. What does the Harvard Study of Adult Development conclude about what makes humans happy and healthy?
8. What does it mean to "lean into" relationships? How can we lean into our relationship with our Maker?
9. In what ways do the laws of nature serve as signifiers?
10. How does the parable of The Prodigal Son illustrate the action of signifiers?
11. Describe a time when you received a powerful expression of unconditional love. What impact did it have on you?

ENDNOTES

1. Erik Rietveld and Julian Kiverstein, "A Rich Landscape of Affordances," *Ecological Psychology* 26:4 (2014): 325.

2. Rietveld and Kiverstein, "A Rich Landscape of Affordances," 344–45.

3. https://imagine.gsfc.nasa.gov/ask_astro/cosmology.html.

4. Hugh Ross, *Beyond the Cosmos: The Transdimensionality of God*, 3rd ed. (Covina, CA: RTB Press, 2017).

5. James Gibson, *The Ecological Approach to Visual Perception* (Boston: Houghton Mifflin, 1986): 129.

6. Edward S. Reed, "The Intention to Use a Specific Affordance: A Framework for Psychology," in *Development in Context: Acting and Thinking in Specific Environments*, ed. R. Wozniak and K. Fisscher (Hillsdale, NJ: Erlbaum, 1993), 62, 68.

7. Reed, "Intention to Use a Specific Affordance," 65.

8. Rob Withagen, Harjo J. de Poel, Duarte Araújo, and Gert-Jan Pepping, "Affordances Can Invite Behavior: Reconsidering the Relationship between Affordances and Agency," *New Ideas in Psychology* 30 (2012), 250.

9. Withagen et al., "Affordances Can Invite Behavior," 256.

10. Neil deGrasse Tyson, *Death by Black Hole: And Other Cosmic Quandaries* (New York: Norton and Company, 2007): 359.

11. World Health Organization, http://www.who.int/gho/mortality_burden_disease/life_tables/situation_trends/en/.

12. Robert Waldinger, Ted Talks (January 25, 2016), https://www.youtube.com/watch?v=8KkKuTCFvzI&t=386s.

13. Waldinger, Ted Talks.

14. Waldinger, Ted Talks.

15. Psalm 68:6 says, "God sets the lonely in families."

16. Matthew 22:37–39.

17. C. S. Lewis, *Mere Christianity* (New York: Harper Collins, 2015): 1–33.

18. Genesis 3:16–19.

19. Hugh Ross, *Why the Universe Is the Way It Is* (Grand Rapids, MI: Baker, 2008), 169–70.

20. Gary Chapman, *The 5 Love Languages: The Secret to Love that Lasts* (Chicago: Northfield, 2015). Chapman describes the five love languages as words of affirmation, quality time, gift giving, acts of service, and physical touch. After reading this book, it occurred to me that at this point in our fledgling relationship with our Maker, God's love language (the clearest expression of our love for God) is obedience. The Bible confirms this idea in John 14:15.

21. Luke 15:11–32.

CHAPTER TWELVE

God as Father, Gardener, Shepherd, Refiner, or Process Engineer

GARDENING IN MY BLOOD

One of the steady and enduring joys of my adult life has been discovered in the tending of our family vegetable garden. We're blessed with a relatively long growing season in Oklahoma, compared to that of northern Indiana where I grew up. Some years are better than others for growing vegetables, but 2007 was fantastic. The tomato plants in our garden were already ten feet tall and it was only the first week of July! We had quickly devoured the first batch of fresh salsa by June. Homemade salsa with chips is a great way to get your kids to eat more vegetables, and we enjoy making it every summer with the produce from our garden.

It's usually late February when the mercury begins to climb in Oklahoma and I feel a strong urge to plant, especially if it's particularly rainy. It still might freeze so I'll put in spinach, radishes, chard, and such, followed by tomatoes, peppers, and green onions in late March. I can't explain why, but I feel like I've just got to have seeds and seedlings in the ground in the early spring or I'm wasting all those good spring rains that so often fall on all that fertile soil in our backyard. Once I have all the crops planted, I sense a relief and profound satisfaction, like my money is in the bank and earning a wonderfully undeserved return on investment. I find myself rejoicing in the rain or the sun, knowing they are both contributing to the miracle of plant life, faithfully occurring just below the surface of our backyard.

However, the first week of a recent April, I was not rejoicing in the weather. I had already put the wire rebar cages over about forty tomato and pepper seedlings when the weather forecast called for a week of cold temperatures, including an extremely hard freeze on the night before Easter. I did not want to lose my investment. So I racked my brain trying to come up with a way to save the seedlings. I finally hit upon an idea that seemed quite reasonable to me. I took off the cylindrical cages and laid them down in rows so the approximately one-foot-tall seedlings came up between the wires into a series of mesh tunnels. Then I covered the tunnels and closed off the ends with nearly all the sleeping bags, blankets, and towels that we owned. Finally, my wife and daughters were gracious enough to contribute to the effort by allowing me to borrow the electric blankets off of their beds for that night. As you probably already figured out, I then tucked the electric blankets around the seedlings inside the tunnels and kept them on "high" all night long. It worked great and the seedlings were saved; however, I did spend Easter evening at the local laundromat returning our bedding and towels to a more acceptable condition. See Figure 12–1.

The interesting thing is that the tomatoes and peppers grew and produced better that year than any other year I can remember. Of course, it could be due to the unusually wet spring or the generous donation of compost from my neighbor. But could it also be that the plants were strengthened by just the right amount of adversity? We know that an appropriate amount of adversity, when received with the right attitude, tends to build strength and productivity in many areas of our lives. This leads me to consider the idea that God has engineered his creation to serve as a kind of refinery that purifies and strengthens his devotees.

A recurring theme in Scripture is of a God who refines his people in the furnace of affliction. Allowing the disciplines of science, engineering, technology, and history to interact with those of biblical literature, theology, and philosophy, this model of God as an early version of today's

Figure 12–1   Tomatoes and Peppers Bedded Down for the Night of the Easter Freeze
Source: Dominic Halsmer

process systems engineer will now be explored in hopes of shedding light on problems in the areas of special divine action and theodicy (why a good God allows so much evil and suffering). This model differs from that of a divine craftsman since a process systems engineer maintains intimate involvement and interaction with the intended product throughout the refining process, in order to maximize the probability of achieving the desired results.

Investigating metallurgical technology from the biblical era sheds light on who God is and what He does. Although a model of God as process engineer has its limits, it may nevertheless be helpful. God has chosen to reveal himself in categories and images to which humans can relate. Both Scripture and nature can assist in furthering our knowledge of God, and deepening our relationship with Him.

What Is God Like?

In a poignant scene from the new movie *Mary Magdalene*, Mary, played by Rooney Mara, asks Jesus, played by Joaquin Phoenix, "How does it feel to be one with God?" Obviously pleased by Mary's feminine curiosity about his emotions, Jesus smiles and says, "No one has ever asked me how it feels."[1] Such a probing question reveals Mary's desire to know Jesus (and God) not only better, but on a personal level. Problems in divine action deal with how God acts in the world; especially in relating to human beings. In order to gain a better understanding of how God acts, or how God is likely to act in a particular situation, it is helpful to consider what kind of person this triune Christian God is. In considering whether a given human being will respond to some stimulus in a particular way, one would certainly want to know what kind of person he or she is. People behave differently, depending not only on their background and capabilities, but also on their personalities.

Though not an incontrovertible law, scientists and engineers are often introverted or drawn toward their own thoughts and inventions, as opposed to seeking out the company and conversations of others. Whereas those attracted to the fields of business and marketing, for example, are often found networking or making connections with others that result in positive possibilities for the future. Thus, knowing whether someone is introverted or extroverted is important if one is trying to predict social behavior.

Now, all this would be quite useless in assisting our understanding of God and how he acts if he is not a personal being, and humans were not made in his image with some capacity for apprehending his personalities. But, according to Christian theology, God *is* personal and we *are* made in his image. Furthermore, God has chosen to reveal himself in categories and images with which humans have firsthand and intimate understandings. Therefore, a fundamental thesis of this chapter is: If one wants to know how God is predisposed to act, one should get to know him on a personal level. To this end, it seems that the special revelation of Scripture may be more helpful than the general revelation of nature. However, though creation may be less personal, what God has made also lends insight into his character and serves to corroborate conclusions from Scripture.

The Bible presents a rich and multifaceted portrait of God, whose depths may never be completely plumbed by mere mortals. But one of humanity's chief purposes is to know God, and believers can look forward to the bliss of pursuing this relationship for all eternity. One of the primary ways that God has already revealed himself to mankind is as Maker, including all of the ongoing implications of that role. Although God rested from his acts of creation on the "seventh day," it is clear from Scripture that his involvement with creation, and mankind in particular, did not cease at that point. On the contrary, the Bible often speaks of God's intimate involvement with his people through both good times and bad times. Even so, the precise manner and means of his involvement may not always be evident from a human perspective.

An example of God's involvement at a difficult time in Israel's history occurred during their long period of slavery and ensuing Exodus from Egypt. Three times in Scripture, God is described as one who brought his people out of Egypt, referring to that experience as an iron-smelting furnace (Deut 4:20, 1 Kings 8:51, Jer 11:4). It is interesting that the formation of Israel as a cohesive people occurred at about the same time in history as humans were discovering how to forge iron implements from iron ore through the use of these specialized heating devices.[2]

This kind of technological development is recognized as significant in the history of mankind, with ancient time periods being labeled as "stone age," "bronze age," and "iron age," depending on the current prevailing technology. And the iron-smelting furnace was the high technology of the early Jewish era, comparable to smartphones or the computer internet of today. And the ancient smith played a similar role to the process engineer of today. Indeed, many places in Scripture refer to the image of metallurgy in describing how God interacts with his people. This image and its implications will be further explored in what follows in an effort to find meaning in adversity.

The Biblical Basis for a Model of God as Refiner

Recall from Chapter Three that both scientists and theologians use models to help them understand reality. Philosopher Thomas J. Oord writes, "Theologians and scientists use models to explore the validity and fruitfulness of competing theories."[3] He explores several models of God's providence in his recent book, *The Uncontrolling Love of God: An Open and Relational Account of Providence*. He also offers an insightful definition of "model" originally articulated by Frederick Ferre: a model is "that which provides epistemological vividness or immediacy to a theory by offering as an interpretation of the abstract or unfamiliar theory structure something that fits the logical form of the theory and is well known."[4] In other words, a good model makes the theoretical understandable by relating it to something familiar.

The Bible employs a rich diversity of imagery in describing God. He is depicted as love, light, king, shepherd, lamb, friend, bridegroom, gardener, father, mother (see Isaiah 49:15), and refiner, among others. Philosopher of religion Ian Ramsey argued that these models are not to be viewed in isolation, but interact with and qualify each other.[5] Theologian Alister McGrath adds that each of these models illuminates certain aspects of our understanding of God and salvation. Although no model is exhaustive in itself, taken together they provide a comprehensive and consistent understanding.[6] His use of the word "comprehensive" here should not be taken to mean "complete," but rather, "broad in scope." He provides the following example for further clarification,

> To speak of "God as shepherd" is thus to affirm that "God is *like* a shepherd." In other words, the image of a shepherd helps us think about the nature of God, and allows us to gain insights into his nature. It does not mean that God is *identical* to a human shepherd. Rather, it means that some aspects of a human shepherd help us think about God more effectively.[7]

In many ways, the models of shepherd and refiner (or process systems engineer) are similar. They both speak of an overseer who is intimately involved in caring for his/her charge. Indeed, the process systems engineer is often tasked with maintaining, or adjusting, operating conditions (such as various temperatures, pressures, and flow rates) so that the engineered product (such as gasoline or plastics) efficiently reaches its intended state. In a sense, the skilled process engineer successfully "shepherds" the product through the process.[8] Though similar, the shepherdly image emphasizes a nurturing and caring relationship,[9] while the engineering image emphasizes God's wisdom and skill, in allowing us to pass through the "refining fires" of this life, and come through for the better. However, both images provide encouragement and reassurance in the midst of trials.

According to McGrath, the three main models of God as Maker are emanation (an overflowing of creative energy), artistic expression, and construction (or engineering). In expounding on this third facet, McGrath writes,

> Many biblical passages portray God as a master builder [or engineer], deliberately constructing the world (for example, Psalm 127:1). The imagery is powerful, conveying the idea of purpose, planning, and a deliberate intention to create. The image is important, in that it draws attention to both the creator and the creation. In addition to bringing out the skill of the creator, it also allows the beauty and ordering of the resulting creation to be appreciated, both for what it is in itself, and for its testimony to the creativity and care of its creator.[10]

Helping Christians appreciate the skill of the Maker, as seen in nature, plays an important role in the strengthening of their faith.[11] Theologian Dennis Cheek has recently engaged in an exploration of the interactions between theology and technology. His insights are also helpful in considering a model of God as process engineer. Along these lines, he writes:

> The concept of technology is not foreign to the Bible; in its canonical form, it is replete with references to ancient technologies of many types. God is sometimes presented in the Old Testament in a manner that we would today call a *systems engineer*. He creates (designs) a universe and world and places within it creatures, including human beings . . . The New Testament continues this theme of technologies . . . The sacrificial death of Jesus is presented as an act that was designed (in modern parlance "engineered") and sanctioned by God as a means to present a spotless "Lamb" who takes upon himself the sins of the world.[12]

We may not normally think of God as one who "engineers" our redemption, as Cheek suggests, but in a general sense, engineers simply arrange things in order to accomplish their purposes. We see a hint of this in the wise woman of Tekoa's messianic response to King David, "Like water spilled on the ground, which cannot be recovered, so we must die. But that is not what God desires; rather, he devises ways [or engineers a solution] so that a banished person does not remain estranged from him" (II Samuel 14:14). How has God engineered the world to assist in his redemptive plan?

Of course, redemption immediately invokes images of the cross of Christ, and rightly so. But God has also engineered various facets of this universe to play important roles in our redemption. God appears to be using the universal experience of adversity to teach humans vital truths that, perhaps, may not be obtained by any other means. Scripture contains many examples of this idea, including Psalm 119:71—"It was good for me to be afflicted, so that I might learn your decrees," and Isaiah 38:17—"Surely it was for my benefit that I suffered such anguish." It seems likely that occasions of adversity, if received with humility, make us more receptive to God's redemptive plan for our lives. And as a result of his redeeming power, we become useful tools in his hands. These ideas are repeatedly illustrated in the many verses that liken God's work in our lives to a refining process:

Deut 4:20   The LORD took you and brought you out of the iron-smelting furnace, out of Egypt.

1 Kg 8:51   your people, whom you brought out of Egypt, out of that iron-smelting furnace

Jer 11:4   your ancestors when I brought them out of Egypt, out of the iron-smelting furnace

Jer 9:7   I will refine and test them, for what else can I do because of the sin of my people?

Is 1:25   I will thoroughly purge away your dross and remove all your impurities.

Ps 66:10   For you, God, tested us; you refined us like silver.

Ps 66:12   We went thru fire . . .but you brought us to a place of abundance.

Is 48:10   See, I have refined you . . . I have tested you in the furnace of affliction.

Mal 3:2   For he will be like a refiner's fire or a launderer's soap.

Mal 3:3   He will sit as a refiner and purifier of silver . . . and refine them like gold & silver.

Ez 22:20   As [metals] are gathered into a furnace to be melted . . . so will I gather and melt you.

Ez 22: 22   As silver is melted in a furnace, so you'll be melted.

Pr 17:3   The crucible for silver and the furnace for gold, but the Lord tests the heart.

Pr 27:21   The crucible for silver and the furnace for gold, but people are tested by their praise.

Jer 6:27   I have made you a tester of metals and my people the ore, that you may . . . test them.

Jer 6:29   The bellows blows . . . to burn away the lead . . . but the refining goes on in vain.

Dan 11:35   Some of the wise will stumble, so they may be refined, purified and made spotless.

Dan 12:10   Many will be purified, made spotless and refined.

Zech 13:9   I will put them into the fire; I will refine them like silver and test them like gold.

Matt 3:11   He will baptize you with the Holy Spirit and fire.

John 15:2   He cuts off every fruitless branch, while every branch that does bear fruit he prunes.

Heb 12:29   for our "God is a consuming fire. . ."

1 Cor 3:13 It will be revealed with fire, and the fire will test the quality of each person's work.

The Refining Furnace and the Divine Smith

Many of the Old Testament passages refer to the use of specialized furnaces for iron-smelting and purification of precious metals. As mentioned earlier, the forging of iron weapons and tools was new technology at the time of Israel's forming as a nation. Expert knowledge and skill were necessary to produce these advanced implements that were used for the production of food and protection from enemies. Research into the early iron-smelting process of that era reveals a very labor intensive activity, in which an early version of a process engineer was intimately involved in continually maintaining the right conditions. An extremely hot combustion chamber was necessary to exceed the melting point of iron (1537°C).

Bellows were frequently employed to provide enough oxygen for the combustion process. Carbon was repeatedly added to draw the oxygen from the iron ore, and in the right amounts to produce iron and steel. A suitable flux was added during reheating and hammering processes to remove the impurities (dross). Quenching and tempering (reheating to lower temperatures) processes were employed to produce hard and durable iron alloys.[13] The implication is that success in this metallurgical engineering venture required not only the skill and resources, but also the careful attention, of a wise and experienced smith who was familiar with the latest technologies.

Religious studies professor Paula McNutt provides insight into the biblical symbolism of the refining process in her book, *The Forging of Israel: Iron TecÚology, Symbolism, and Tradition in Ancient Society.* She describes the key image of a divine smith who accomplishes transformation in his creation, by allowing that creation to experience adversity with appropriate mediation.[14] It is a vivid picture of a Maker who not only creates and maintains the right conditions in the universe to afford the opportunity for human transformation, but also enters into that universe to participate in the adversity and mediate an ultimate solution to the human condition. The next section will further explore this imagery by addressing concerns associated with theodicy (the problem of evil and suffering in the world) and divine action (how a spiritual being acts to accomplish purposes in the physical world).

Refined for Relationship

Notice that the first three verses from the above list (Deut 4:20, 1 Kg 8:51, and Jer 11:4) all refer to Israel's time of slavery in Egypt as a period of refinement as in an "iron-smelting furnace." But that is not the only thing these passages have in common. Upon closer inspection of the immediate context in each case, it becomes clear why God allows his people to experience such adversity. It is for the relationship they are to have with their Maker. This idea is expressed by many of the other verses as well. God refines us so that we are fit to experience the fullness of an intimate relationship with him. We are still in process, and although we are saved by the death and resurrection of Christ, God somehow uses the difficult experiences of this life to refine, or sanctify us, preparing us for an eternity with our Maker.

Process engineers know that refining methods that produce valuable metal alloys make use of key relational aspects of creation to generate desirable characteristics such as hardness, durability, and toughness. These features, when present in a forged tool or weapon, afford the user increased efficiency and capability for the task at hand. In a similar way, our Maker allows us to experience adversity because it produces valuable, if not vital, affordances in human beings.[15] And according to 1 Corinthians 10:13, he will not test us beyond our ability to endure.

When received with humility, in a redemptive environment (thanks to Jesus), we see how adversity often results in strength, resilience, endurance, and a greater knowledge of the truth. In addition, philosopher of religion Richard Swinburne writes that difficult circumstances provide us with significant opportunities to show compassion and kindness to others that we might not have under any other circumstances.[16] Again, we see how adversity brings opportunity for enhancing relationships.

Furthermore, strength, and even growth, in the midst of adversity appears to provide testimony that God knows what he's doing. Paul writes to the Thessalonians,

We ought always to thank God for you, brothers and sisters, and rightly so, because your faith is growing more and more, and the love all of you have for one another is increasing. Therefore, among God's churches we boast about your perseverance and faith in all the persecutions and trials you are enduring. All this is evidence that God's judgment is right, and as a result you will be counted worthy of the kingdom of God, for which you are suffering. (2 Thessalonians 1:3–5)

The Thessalonians were experiencing persecutions and trials, and yet their faith and love were increasing. Paul claims that this shows that God's calculations are correct, even justifying the Maker's wisdom in allowing evil and suffering to persist for a season. Indeed, history shows that the early church, in Rome especially, grew rapidly during extreme persecution, largely because of the joyful testimony of the suffering faithful, even unto martyrdom! It seems that adversity may play a key role in solidifying a believer's trust in God, ultimately committing him/her to always choose the good, true, and beautiful out of love for their Maker.

Finally, adversity appears to afford opportunities for God to break through (special divine action) and encourage his people when they really need it. In 2 Corinthians, Paul writes about his tormenting "thorn in the flesh," which was evidently so bad that he pleaded with God three times to remove it. It is interesting to note that God did not remove it, but instead *spoke* to Paul. He said, "My grace is sufficient for you, for my power is made perfect in weakness" (2 Corinthians 12:9). I don't know whether Paul heard an audible voice on that occasion, but somehow God broke through (from the supernatural to the natural) in a way that made all the difference, and provided an important lesson about adversity to benefit the church for the rest of time.

I'm not suggesting that special divine action such as this happens a lot, but testimonies abound within the church on how God somehow communicates with his children in unmistakable ways. I'm also not suggesting that this is something that can easily be quantified or studied scientifically. But I know it when I see it, or when I experience it for myself. On multiple occasions in the last few years, I have found myself in very difficult places at critical points in my life. And God communicated profound and life-changing encouragement and wisdom to me in the midst of those challenging circumstances. I didn't hear an audible voice or experience a documented miracle. But in these situations, I knew beyond a reasonable doubt that I had "heard" from God, even if in a somewhat mysterious way. The reason I say this is because of the good and ongoing fruit that resulted in these cases due to my complete change in attitude and mental/emotional state.

Basically, due to unusual events, I surprisingly and immediately found myself with the joy, courage, and power to carry on with the work to which I had been called. Due to the personal nature of these events, it is with some hesitation that I share the details of one of them in the next section. But I think it is important to recount this experience as a witness to God's intimate concern and involvement with us in the midst of the refinement process.

Personal Experience of Special Divine Action

About eight years ago, I was beginning to spend more time conducting research in the area of science and faith and less time in engineering. It seemed to me that the Lord was leading me in this direction, even though I continued to enjoy teaching engineering courses at Oral Roberts University. I was also beginning to see how the field of engineering might have important contributions to make to the science and theology conversation.

I was working on a PowerPoint presentation at home one evening on my laptop computer at our dining room table. The presentation was on science and faith to be delivered the following day at a seminar for which I had volunteered. I remember being somewhat overwhelmed with everything that was "on my plate" at that particular time in my career. And I began to wonder if I was doing the right thing by spending time researching and presenting in science and faith. I wasn't getting much encouragement or support from any direction at this time, and I was beginning to doubt what I had thought was a call into this area.

On top of all that, I was struggling to use a piece of software that was supposed to easily capture video clips for insertion into PowerPoint presentations. But it was not working out very well. It captured the video fine, but an external microphone was needed to grab the audio, and the sound was not coming through loud and clear. I remember getting extremely frustrated with the whole project, sitting there at the table in a very dejected state of mind, wondering if I was just wasting my time.

It was about then that our youngest daughter, Josie, came in the front door from high school basketball practice. Partly to get a break from my unsuccessful attempts to craft an exciting presentation, I offered to make her some supper, remembering that there was some leftover rice in the refrigerator. She said she would eat some fried rice, so I pulled it out, along with an egg and some vegetables. I put a skillet on the stove top and turned on the heat.

I must not have been paying close attention to what I was doing. My mind was probably still fretting over all the things I had to do, including the pressing presentation for the next day. When I grabbed the bottle of olive oil, I shook it for some unknown reason, like it was an oil and vinegar salad dressing that needed to be reconstituted before using. That was stupid because it was just olive oil, without the slightest need for shaking. And again, for some unknown reason, the cap on the bottle was loose, and olive oil went everywhere!

For an instant, this was like the straw that broke the camel's back. Really God? This is what I get for trying to serve others? A big mess to clean up, meaning even less time to tend to all my urgent responsibilities. I stood there in the kitchen, my blood beginning to boil, wondering if a primal scream was next on the agenda. What a mess! Some of the oil fell on the floor. Some of it fell on the countertop. Some of it fell on the clean dishes, drying in the sink. Some of it actually fell in the pan. And some of the olive oil fell . . . on . . . my . . . head! Wait a minute. In an instant, my frustration was arrested, my volcano of rage immediately became inactive, and an inexplicable joy and peace began to flood my heart.

Why did I experience this sudden change of emotions? Because I had been working on a master's degree in biblical literature, and I understood the significance of having olive oil dumped on one's head. I smiled as I thought to myself, "I know what this means. It means that I am anointed." I actually began to laugh at the completely ridiculous idea that through my own stupidity, God had somehow managed to anoint me with the bottle of olive oil from our kitchen cabinet. And yet, here I was, with a complete reversal of emotions, and newfound energy, enthusiasm, and delight to carry on the work to which I had been called.

I immediately thought of Jesus's words in Luke 4:18–19: "The Spirit of the Lord is on me, because he has anointed me to proclaim good news to the poor. He has sent me to proclaim freedom for the prisoners and recovery of sight for the blind, to set the oppressed free, to proclaim the year of the Lord's favor." It was as if a new realization of how these verses could describe the impact of my work had suddenly been downloaded to my brain. I couldn't stop laughing as I reveled in the thought that, even though no mentor or friend was available to anoint me, God himself had somehow pulled it off. I know it sounds silly, and perhaps it was all in my head, and God actually didn't do anything. But that doesn't really make sense when considering the fruit, or the outcome, of the event. I went from deep depression to abundant joy; from paralyzing frustration to energized inspiration, virtually in an instant. That just doesn't happen accidently or through human willpower.

After a while, I came to understand that this message of special anointing was not just for myself, but for the entire faculty at Oral Roberts University. I seized the opportunity at a subsequent university faculty assembly meeting to remind the faculty and administration that, even when we feel alone, inept, or unappreciated, we are anointed to complete the work to which God has called us. This message was received with gratitude and generally found to be very encouraging. The significance of these events for the larger community provides another reason to believe that God was indeed communicating something special to me through these weird circumstances. In addition, years of successful, fulfilling, and productive work in the area of science and faith since this event continue to confirm this understanding.

I have also experienced other instances of what I believe to have been divine action. During the incident involving the BioLogos grant (described in Chapter 2), I was in a very tight spot with the administration at ORU and I prayed hard for guidance. I believe God clearly spoke to me through a dream and a song, but this affair is too personal to share in this format. Perhaps if you catch me face-to-face and ask me about it, I would be willing to share some of the details. It reminded me of a time when my dad was in a tight spot and believed that he had received direction from God through a vision of Jesus.

Although raised Catholic and still attending Catholic church, after his renewal experience, he and my mom had been meeting regularly with believers from other denominations to pray and study the Bible. They quickly became a very close-knit group. A few Methodists in the group invited my parents to join them on a mission trip to Central America to help build a church, and they decided to go. But on the way down, as my Dad was driving one of the vehicles, he began to wonder if he was doing the right thing; a Catholic helping to build a Methodist church?! On top of that, they became lost and literally didn't know if they were heading in the right direction. As my dad prayed for divine guidance while heading down a road, suddenly in the distance he saw a man in a long flowing white robe standing up on an embankment beside the road, with arm outstretched, pointing in the direction they were heading. Dad recalled that he could see every detail of this person's features, but as they got closer, the body of the man became a portion of deteriorating tree trunk, and the man's outstretched arm became the last remaining branch. He concluded that his prayers had been answered, and that not only were they going the right way, but that he and my mom were doing the right thing by facilitating unity among Christians in this way. For more accounts of special divine action, see the biography of my dad's life, *Chosen to Fly*, by Josephine Halsmer, published by the Apple Tree Press in 1992.

Trust the Engineer of Your Soul

If God is a personal being and humans are made in his image, then he has enabled humans to know him to a significant degree, even in this life. God reveals himself, both in Scripture and in nature, using categories and images that humans can understand. A powerful image from Scripture is of a refiner, or process systems engineer. Experience with these technologies clarifies this image and helps in knowing God better. Though no image is perfect, a model of God as refiner, or process systems engineer, is a useful biblical and theological construct based on scientific principles and engineering applications. Characteristics of the ancient iron-smelting process indicate that the smith (or process engineer) was intimately involved in "fathering" or "shepherding" the product through the difficult refining process. The biblical picture is one of a divine Smith whose skill and wisdom are seen in a universe with just the right amount of built-in adversity, which affords the transformation of willing humans, with appropriate mediation through the incarnation, life, death, and resurrection of Christ.

This provides some measure of relief to the problem of theodicy since, as a result of this model we can more easily see God's wisdom and skill in turning evil and adversity around, and causing it to work for our good. In particular, we notice that God is refining us for a wonderful and eternal loving relationship with himself. Theologian Hans Urs von Balthasar writes insightfully of how our love is empowered and refined through testing, "Love makes us free if it is selfless, and it is selfless if it is ready to sacrifice pleasure, advantage and independence for the sake of the beloved. And since no earthly love is initially perfect, it must go through these purifications. Moments and times must come when love is tested through sacrifice, when it becomes clear whether the enthusiasm of the first encounter was love at all, when the naïve first love—if it really was love—is refined and deepened in the fire of renunciation."[17]

The picture that emerges from a reverse engineering approach to understanding the cosmos is one that illustrates the multiple purposes of the Maker. These purposes are accomplished through the single complex vehicle known as our multifaceted universe. Recall the high level of ingenuity associated with a single device that simultaneously satisfies multiple diverse purposes. First, the cosmos affords the emergence of life that is capable of knowing its Maker. Second, the cosmos provides knowledge of the Maker through affordances that demonstrate ingenuity, wisdom, and loving care. And third, the cosmos has been engineered to invite us into an everlasting loving relationship with our Maker. From our intimate knowledge of the human condition, it appears that this entails a significant level of disease, discomfort, and death for a season. But the magnificent ingenuity displayed in nature gives us good reason to trust the Maker. Indeed, the negatives of the human condition make sense if the Maker is demonstrating a "subtract and operate" procedure[18] to "drive home" the idea that only isolation and hopelessness result from choosing sinful pride and rebellion instead of the ultimate relationship that fulfills our purpose.

Finally, the author's experiences of divine communication and encouragement in the midst of the heat of refinement testify to the ongoing care and loving-kindness of our Maker during the process. Thus, God's kindness assists us greatly during trials, and leads us to repentance (Romans 2:4). In this way, the universe seems to be engineered to woo us away from depending solely on our own resources, and instead, place trust in our Maker, and the wisdom of his redemptive plan.

A SUMMERTIME CHRISTMAS TREE

When my siblings and I were young, our parents put us to work doing chores that contributed to the success of our home. It was an annoyance at the time, but through that adversity we learned to enjoy the satisfaction and fruit of our labors. One of our jobs was to tend the family garden, and at the time I hated it, especially pulling weeds. It's funny how I find that same activity quite satisfying, even therapeutic, today.

We did try to find ways to make gardening more enjoyable back then. My parents also loved homegrown tomatoes, but for some reason, they never used cages and often the ripening tomatoes would develop bad spots while sitting on the ground. There was a general understanding among the children whenever one came across this situation. Such "rotten" tomatoes were to be immediately picked and flung, with all the strength and intensity of a major league pitcher, at the "Christmas tree." As everyone in our family knew, our summertime Christmas tree was a large shagbark hickory that stood on the north side of our garden, sporting numerous tomato splotches in various states of decomposition due to the aforementioned activity. One of the coveted badges of accomplishment in our family was the ability to properly decorate the Christmas tree from any of the far corners of our garden whenever the situation arose. It quickly became my favorite part of helping in the garden, and I recall searching high and low for tomatoes with bad spots.

Sadly, this tradition has not been continued in our garden in Oklahoma, since I now value homegrown tomatoes a lot more than I did as a kid. As a result, I tend to trim off any bad spots and consume the remainder. Furthermore, our tradition of decorating the Christmas tree tended to regress into more unacceptable altercations. I don't know exactly how it started. It may have been due to the fact that when throwing a rotten tomato with all your might, it sometimes behaves more like a shotgun blast than a rifle bullet or a baseball. It may have been that one of the children accidentally decorated a sibling while attempting to decorate the Christmas tree. All I know for sure is that an all-out tomato war broke out in our garden during prime tomato picking season on more than one occasion. Bad and good tomatoes alike filled the air and I remember that after we finally got it stopped, my brother's white t-shirt was soaking red with tomato juice. The rest of us found ourselves in a similar state of juiciness, and we were all in big trouble.

My mother was a very thrifty person, making the most of what we had to satisfy all thirteen children and her husband. She insisted on good stewardship of the resources and gifts we had been given. So you can imagine how this kind of stupid waste was intolerable for her. She passed these traits of thriftiness and stewardship onto me and I didn't even realize it until I was older. She insisted that we eat all the food that we took at meals, and to this day it is difficult for me to leave food on my plate. I find myself scraping the mixing bowl or food container to get every last bit of product out. I try to utilize every square foot of my garden in an effort to maximize the productivity of my modest plots. I've designed a wire mesh structure that connects my rows of tomato cages with a half-cylindrical canopy at the top. In this way the giant plants don't fall over and get kinked, but can continue to climb and produce well into November or December if the first freeze comes late.

I'm grateful to my mother for demonstrating this kind of stewardship and faithfulness, and instilling it in me. She is a prime example of one who grew strong and productive in the midst of adversity, even into her later years. I can see how her character and spirit continue to grow stronger, even as the outward shell of her body wastes away. God knows just the right amount of adversity to allow in our lives. The Scriptures teach that he even measures or calculates how much to allow. Like a brilliant engineer, He's able to cause it all to work together for our good, if we are willing to respond to His call, and submit to his magnificent designs for us.

It appears that God allows humans beings to experience adversity because, when received with humility in a redemptive environment, it tends to produce certain positive affordances in the human system, which are necessary for an ongoing fruitful relationship with the Maker. Furthermore, the fruit of increasing faith, hope, and love in the midst of affliction affords testimony of God's wisdom in allowing disharmony to persist for a season. Often, this is accomplished via God-ordained natural laws, but sometimes humans need special grace that is only realized through the unmistakable nature of special divine action. Either way, in sincere gratitude we can proclaim, along with the famous droid from *Star Wars* fame, C3PO, "Thank the Maker!"[19]

Figure 12–2   Droid C3PO Thanks the Maker when It Is Discovered That Han Solo Has Survived Being Frozen in Carbonite
© Krikkiat/Shutterstock.com

STUDY QUESTIONS

1. Describe a time when you invested in something or someone that payed off. What did you learn from this experience?

2. How does a model of God as Process Systems Engineer differ from a model of God as Craftsman?

3. In what ways does God's personality display aspects of an extrovert? Introvert? Do you think he is more one way than the other? Give reasons to support your assertion.

4. What reasons would you present (from nature and Scripture) to support the idea that God is a personal being who desires a personal relationship with each of us?

5. What is the significance of the multiple scriptural references to the Israelites time in Egypt as an "iron-smelting furnace"?

6. How does a good model make a complex and theoretical reality more understandable?

7. How should the many different scriptural images of God be viewed?

8. Compare and contrast the models of God as shepherd and refiner.

9. According to McGrath, why is a model of God important?

10. In what sense was Jesus's death and resurrection a beautiful solution to a spiritual engineering design problem?

11. What reasons would you present (from nature and Scripture) to support the idea that God allows adversity for our ultimate benefit, using it to woo, refine, and sanctify us?

12. Study the many scriptures (in context) on God as refiner and look for multiple subthemes. Group each of the passages into one of these subthemes.

13. In what ways was the early iron-smelting process a very labor-intensive activity?

14. How does McNutt's image of a divine smith help us understand what God is doing in the universe, and in our lives?

15. Why would God allow his people to experience the adversity of an iron-smelting furnace?

16. Cite three New Testament passages and explain how they offer reassurances that help us to trust God in the midst of testing and adversity.

17. What is one good indicator that someone has probably "heard from God"? Do you think this applies to the founding of Oral Roberts University? Why or why not?

18. Describe a time when you "heard from God." What made you think it was God? What did you learn from this experience?

19. How does a model of God as process systems engineer provide some support to the question of theodicy?

20. Summarize three purposes of the cosmos that arise as a consequence of an affordance-based reverse engineering approach.

21. Explain how the nature of the universe, with particular focus on the human condition, can be seen as a "subtract and operate" illustration from the field of reverse engineering.

22. Describe personality traits that were afforded to you through your family upbringing. Were they mostly "taught" (verbal instruction) or mostly "caught" (by example)? Which of these traits would you like to pass on to your descendants? How will you do this?

ENDNOTES

1. *Mary Magdalene*, Directed by Garth Davis, See Saw Films, London, 2019.

2. Paula M. McNutt, *The Forging of Israel: Iron Tecᴕology, Symbolism, and Tradition in Ancient Society* (Sheffield, UK: Sheffield Academic Press, 1990), 21.

3. Thomas J. Oord, *The Uncontrolling Love of God: An Open and Relational Account of Providence* (Downers Grove, IL: IVP Academic, in press), 78.

4. Frederick Ferre, "Mapping the Logic of Models in Science and Theology," in *New Essays on Religious Language*, ed. Dallas M. High (New York: Oxford University Press, 1969), 75.

5. Ian T. Ramsey, *Models for Divine Activity* (London: SCM Press, 1973).

6. McGrath, *Science and Religion*, 106.

7. Alister McGrath, *Theology: The Basics* (West Sussex, UK: Wiley-Blackwell, 2013), 22.

8. Thanks to a conversation with David L. Wilcox, as a result of the following article, for helping me see this point: David L. Wilcox, "Three Models of Making: Prime Mover, Craftsman, and King—Alternate Theistic Frameworks for Teaching Origins," *Perspectives on Science and Christian Faith* 39 (December 1987): 212.

9. Even so, the actions of a good shepherd may not always be obviously kind, as when a sheep's leg may be intentionally broken to keep it from wandering. In such cases, caring is informed by wisdom. Thanks to an anonymous reviewer for this insight.

10. McGrath, *Theology*, 44.

11. Dominic Halsmer and Caleb Lutz, "Science and the Wisdom of God: Encouraging an Appreciation for the Ingenuity that Underlies our Evolving Universe," in *Genesis and Genetics: Proceedings of the 2014 Faith & Science Conference*, ed. David R. Bundrick and Steve Badger (Springfield, MO: Logion Press, 2014), 353–68.

12. Dennis William Cheek, "Is there Room for the Spirit in a World Dominated by Technology? Pentecostals and the Technological World," in *Science and the Spirit: A Pentecostal Engagement with the Sciences*, ed. Amos Yong (Bloomington, IN: Indiana University, 2010), 194–95.

13. McNutt, *Forging of Israel*, 148–51.

14. McNutt, *Forging of Israel*, 261–67.

15. Dominic Halsmer, Michael Gewecke, Rachelle Gewecke, Nate Roman, Tyler Todd, and Jessica Fitzgerald, "Reversible Universe: Implications of Affordance-based Reverse Engineering of Complex Natural Systems," in *Engineering and the Ultimate: An Interdisciplinary Investigation of Order and Design in Nature and Craft*, ed. Jonathan Bartlett, Dominic Halsmer, and Mark R. Hall (Broken Arrow, OK: Blyth Institute Press, 2014), 11–38.

16. Richard Swinburne, *The Existence of God* (New York: Oxford University Press, 2004), 260–61.

17. Hans Urs von Balthasar, *Prayer* (San Francisco: Ignatius Press, 1986), 128.

18. As a result of mankind's fall, in effect, God removed himself (to a large degree) from the universe, allowing humans to experience the sad but inevitable consequences of "going their own way." It seems reasonable that such a "subtract and operate" illustration may be the best (and perhaps only) way to communicate such a terrifying reality to free-will-endowed creatures. Could this be the most important lesson we glean from the shocking devastation unleashed by the Maker during Noah's flood? (Recall the difficult questions posed in Chapters 9 and 10.) Fortunately for

us, he saw fit to offer the solution, by inserting himself back into the universe at the right time in the person and redemptive work of Jesus Christ.

19. See *Star Wars Episode V: The Empire Strikes Back*, on the occasion when C3PO learns that Han Solo has survived being frozen in carbonite.